National 5

Biology

Practice Papers for SQA Exams

Billy Dickson

Graham Moffat

Contents

Introduction iii
Key Area index grid vi
Practice Paper A 1
Practice Paper B 27
Practice Paper C 51
Answers 79

The instructions and answer grid for completion of Section 1 in each practice paper can be downloaded from www.hoddereducation.co.uk/updatesandextras

The Publishers would like to thank the following for permission to reproduce copyright material:

Exam rubric in Section 1 and Section 2 of each practice paper; online instructions and marking grid for completion of Section 1, Copyright © Scottish Qualifications Authority.

Acknowledgements

Every effort has been made to trace all copyright holders, but if any have been inadvertently overlooked the Publishers will be pleased to make the necessary arrangements at the first opportunity.

Although every effort has been made to ensure that website addresses are correct at time of going to press, Hodder Gibson cannot be held responsible for the content of any website mentioned in this book. It is sometimes possible to find a relocated web page by typing in the address of the home page for a website in the URL window of your browser.

Hachette UK's policy is to use papers that are natural, renewable and recyclable products and made from wood grown in sustainable forests. The logging and manufacturing processes are expected to conform to the environmental regulations of the country of origin.

Orders: please contact Bookpoint Ltd, 130 Milton Park, Park Drive, Abingdon, Oxon OX14 4SE. Telephone: (44) 01235 827720. Fax: (44) 01235 400454. Lines are open 9.00–5.00, Monday to Saturday, with a 24-hour message answering service. Visit our website at www.hoddereducation.co.uk. Hodder Gibson can be contacted direct on: Tel: 0141 333 4650; Fax: 0141 404 8188; email: hoddergibson@hodder.co.uk

© Billy Dickson, Graham Moffat 2016

First published in 2016 by
Hodder Gibson, an imprint of Hodder Education,
An Hachette UK Company
211 St Vincent Street
Glasgow G2 5QY

Impression number 5 4 3 2 1
Year 2020 2019 2018 2017 2016

All rights reserved. Apart from any use permitted under UK copyright law, no part of this publication may be reproduced or transmitted in any form or by any means, electronic or mechanical, including photocopying and recording, or held within any information storage and retrieval system, without permission in writing from the publisher or under licence from the Copyright Licensing Agency Limited. Further details of such licences (for reprographic reproduction) may be obtained from the Copyright Licensing Agency Limited, Saffron House, 6–10 Kirby Street, London EC1N 8TS.

Cover photo © Sebastian Duda/Fotolia
Illustrations by Aptara Inc.
Typeset in India by Aptara Inc.
Printed and bound by CPI Group (UK) Ltd, Croydon, CR0 4YY

A catalogue record for this title is available from the British Library

ISBN: 978 1 4718 8591 4

Introduction

National 5 Biology

The three papers included in this book are designed to provide practice and to support revision for the National 5 Biology course assessment question paper (the examination), which is worth 80% of the final grade for this course.

Together, the three papers give overall and comprehensive coverage of Demonstrating and Applying Knowledge and the Skills of Scientific Inquiry needed to pass National 5 Biology.

Design of the papers

Each paper has been carefully assembled to be very similar to a typical National 5 question paper. Each paper has 80 marks and is divided into two sections.

Section 1 – Objective Test, which contains 20 multiple choice items worth 1 mark each and totalling 20 marks altogether.

Section 2 – Paper 2, which contains restricted and extended response questions worth 1 to 4 marks each and totalling 60 marks altogether.

In each paper, the marks are distributed evenly across all three component units of the course and 50–60 marks are for Demonstrating and Applying Knowledge. The remaining 20–30 marks are for the application of Skills of Scientific Inquiry. We have included features of the National Papers such as offering choice in some questions.

In each paper, 70% of the marks are set at the standard of Grade C and the remaining 30% are more difficult marks set at the standard for Grade A. We have attempted to construct each paper to represent the typical range of demand in a National 5 Biology paper.

Key Area index grid

The Key Area index grid on pages 6–8 shows the pattern of coverage of the knowledge in the Key Areas and the Skills across the three papers. We have provided marks totals for each Key Area and each Skill. Scoring more than half of these marks suggests that you have a good grasp of the content of that specific Key Area or Skill.

After having worked on questions from a particular Key Area or Skill, you might want to use the boxes to show progress. We suggest marking like this [–] if you are having difficulty (less than half marks), like this [+] if you have done further work and are more comfortable (more than half marks), and this [*] if you are confident you have learned a particular Key Area or Skill (nearly full marks). Alternatively you could 'traffic light' using colour – red for 'not understood', orange for 'more work needed' and green for 'fully understood'. If you continue to struggle with a set of Key Area or Skills questions, you should see your teacher for extra help.

Student margins

The question pages have 'student margins' in which we have cross referenced each question to the Course Assessment Specification (CAS) for N5 Biology from the SQA website at www.sqa.org.uk and to the Hodder Gibson *How To Pass National 5 Biology* (HTP) book. The margins also have a key to each question to show what is being tested and the level of demand intended, as shown in the table below. For questions worth more than one mark, we have allocated each mark to a demand level. For example, **CA** means one mark at **C** and the second at **A**. For questions testing Skills, we have referenced to the Skills of Scientific Inquiry chapter of *How To Pass*, although the CAS reference is for the Key Area from which the question context was taken.

Key	Meaning
dKU	Demonstrating knowledge and understanding of biology
aKU	Applying knowledge of biology to new situations, interpreting information and solving problems
Planning	Planning or designing experiments to test given hypotheses
Selecting	Selecting information from a variety of sources
Presenting	Presenting information appropriately in a variety of forms
Processing	Processing information using calculations and units where appropriate
Predicting	Making predictions and generalisations based on evidence
Concluding	Drawing valid conclusions and giving explanations supported by evidence
Evaluating	Suggesting improvements to experiments and investigations
C	Basic level of demand linked with Grade C
A	More challenging level of demand linked with Grade A

Using the papers

Each paper can be attempted as a whole, or groups of questions on a particular Key Area or Skill can be tackled – use the Key Area index grid to find related groups of questions. In the grid, questions have been allocated to the main Area being tested. Use the *Date completed* column to keep a record of your progress.

We recommend alternating between attempting the questions and studying the answers (see below). You will find a reference to the location of the answers at the end of each Objective Test and following each Section 2 question.

Where any difficulty is encountered, it is worth trying to consolidate by reading the referenced material from *How To Pass*. Use the information in the student margin to identify the type of question you find most tricky. Be aware that A-type questions are expected to be challenging.

You will need a pen, sharp pencil, clear plastic ruler and a calculator for the best results. A couple of different coloured highlighters could also be handy.

Answers

The expected answers on pages 87–110 give National Standard answers but, occasionally, there may be other acceptable answers. There is a commentary with hints and tips provided alongside each answer. Don't feel you need to use them all!

The commentaries on the answers focus on the biology itself, as well as giving hints and tips, a focus on traditionally difficult areas, advice on wording of answers, and notes of common errors.

Grading

The three papers are designed to be equally demanding and to reflect the National Standard of a typical SQA paper. Each paper has 80 marks – if you score 40 marks that is a C pass. You will need about 48 marks for a B pass and about 56 marks for an A. These figures are a rough guide only.

Timing

If you are attempting a full paper, limit yourself to two hours to complete it. Get someone to time you! We recommend no more than 25 minutes for the Objective Test and the remainder of the time for Section 2.

If you are tackling blocks of questions in a Key Area or Skill, give yourself about a minute and a half per mark; for example, a set of questions worth 10 marks should take about 15 minutes.

Key Area calendar

You could use the Key Area calendar below to plan revision for your final exam. There are 20 Key Areas, so covering two each week would require a 10-week revision programme. The exams are in May, so starting after your February holiday would give you time – just!

Key Area revised	Date	Questions completed (✓)	Green light for confidence! (✓)
1.1 Cell structure			
1.2 Transport across cell membranes			
1.3 Producing new cells			
1.4 DNA and the production of proteins			
1.5 Proteins and enzymes			
1.6 Genetic engineering			
1.7 Photosynthesis			
1.8 Respiration			
2.1 Cells, tissues and organs			
2.2 Stem cells and meristems			
2.3 Control and communication			
2.4 Reproduction			
2.5 Variation and inheritance			
2.6 The need for transport			
2.7 Lifestyle choices	Questions in context of appropriate Key Area		
3.1 Biodiversity and distribution of life			
3.2 Energy in ecosystems			
3.3 Sampling and measurement			
3.4 Adaptation and evolution			
3.5 Human impact on the environment			

Good luck!

Key Area index grid

Skill tested	Key Area or Skill	Practice Paper questions (OT – Objective Test; P2 – Paper 2)			Marks	Traffic light	Date completed
		Paper A	Paper B	Paper C			
Unit 1 **Cell Biology** Demonstrating and Applying Knowledge	1.1 Cell structure	**OT** Q1 **P2** Q1	**OT** Q1,2	**P2** Q1	**/12**		
	1.2 Transport across cell membranes	**OT** Q12	**P2** Q1	**OT** Q1,2	**/8**		
	1.3 Producing new cells	**P2** Q2	**OT** Q3	**P2** Q3a, bi,c	**/8**		
	1.4 DNA and the production of proteins	**OT** Q3 **P2** Q3b	**P2** Q2a,c	**OT** Q3 **P2** Q4	**/11**		
	1.5 Proteins and enzymes	**P2** Q4d	**OT** Q5	**OT** Q4 **P2** Q1c	**/5**		
	1.6 Genetic engineering	**OT** Q7	**P2** Q3	**OT** Q5	**/7**		
	1.7 Photosynthesis	**P2** Q5ai, 6aii,6b	**OT** Q6	**P2** Q5	**/9**		
	1.8 Respiration	**OT** Q5,6	**OT** Q7 **P2** Q4bii	**OT** Q8 **P2** Q3bii	**/6**		

Skill tested	Key Area or Skill	Practice Paper questions (OT – Objective Test; P2 – Paper 2)			Marks	Traffic light	Date completed
		Paper A	Paper B	Paper C			
Unit 2 Multicellular Organisms Demonstrating and Applying Knowledge	2.1 Cells, tissues and organs	**P2** Q7a,b	**OT** Q9,10	**P2** Q6a	/7		
	2.2 Stem cells and meristems	**OT** Q8	**P2** Q5	**OT** Q9	/7		
	2.3 Control and communication	**OT** Q14 **P2** Q8	**OT** Q11,12 **P2** Q6a,b	**P2** Q7	/14		
	2.4 Reproduction	**OT** Q9	**P2** Q7	**P2** Q9b	/5		
	2.5 Variation and inheritance	**OT** Q10 **P2** Q9a, 9b,9d	**OT** Q13,14 **P2** Q8	**OT** Q10,11	/13		
	2.6 The need for transport	**OT** Q11 **P2** Q5aii, iii,10b	**P2** Q9b	**OT** Q12, 13,14,15 **P2** Q6b	/13		
	2.7 Lifestyle choices	Questions relating to this Key Area are found spread into other Areas such as *The need for transport*					
Unit 3 Life on Earth Demonstrating and Applying Knowledge	3.1 Biodiversity and distribution of life	**OT** Q15	**P2** Q10b	**OT** Q16	/4		
	3.2 Energy in ecosystems	**OT** Q18 **P2** Q11	**OT** Q17,18	**P2** Q12	/10		
	3.3 Sampling and measurement	**P2** Q13a,bi	**OT** Q19	**P2** Q10e	/5		
	3.4 Adaptation and evolution	**OT** Q17	**OT** Q20	**P2** Q13	/6		
	3.5 Human impact on the environment	**OT** Q16 **P2** Q12	**P2** Q10c, 11d,12b,c	**OT** Q19 **P2** Q11a, b	/15		

Skill tested	Key Area or Skill	Practice Paper questions (OT – Objective Test; P2 – Paper 2)			Marks	Traffic light	Date completed
		Paper A	Paper B	Paper C			
N5 Biology course Skills of Scientific Inquiry	Planning	**OT** Q13 **P2** Q4ci	**P2** Q4bi, 11a,	**P2** Q2b, 3bii,8a, b,10c	/11		
	Selecting	**OT** Q20 **P2** Q3ai,ii,iv,v, 10aii	**OT** Q8 **P2** Q6cii, 9ai,11c, 12a	**OT** Q7,20 **P2** Q9aii,11c	/18		
	Presenting	**P2** Q4a	**P2** Q4a	**P2** Q2a,10a	/8		
	Processing	**OT** Q19 **P2** Q3aiii, 4b,6ai, 10aiii	**OT** Q4,15, 16 **P2** Q2b,4c, 6ci,9aii,iii	**OT** Q17,18 **P2** Q8d, 9ai,10b	/18		
	Predicting	**OT** Q4 **P2** Q9c	**P2** Q4d	**OT** Q6 **P2** Q2c	/6		
	Concluding	**OT** Q2 **P2** Q5b, 10ai	**P2** Q10a	**P2** Q9aiii,iv, 11d	/9		
	Evaluating	**P2** Q4cii, 13bii	**P2** Q11b	**P2** Q8c,10d	/5		
Marks totals		**80**	**80**	**80**	**240**		

You are now ready to begin working through the practice papers. At the start of Section 1 and Section 2 of each practice paper we have provided instructions on how to complete the paper, similar to those you will read in your exam. Please be aware that these instructions have been adjusted to be more suitable for the revision purposes of this book, but are aimed at preparing you for the final exam. Please visit www.hoddereducation.co.uk/updatesandextras to download full instructions on how to answer Section 1 multiple choice questions. There is also an answer grid for you to practise with.

Practice Paper A

National 5 Biology

HODDER GIBSON
LEARN MORE

Section 1

SECTION 1 — 20 marks

Attempt ALL questions. Answer grid available at www.hoddereducation.co.uk/updatesandextras.

STUDENT MARGIN

1 The diagram below shows a plant leaf cell.

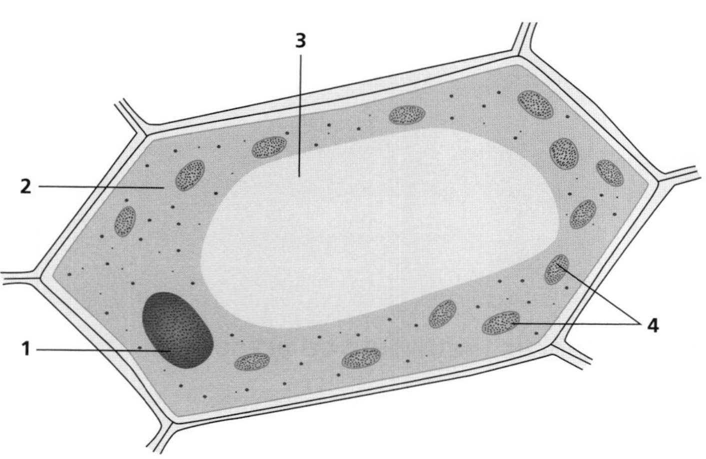

Which line in the table below shows the cell structures in which mRNA and sugar are synthesised?

	Substance	
	mRNA	**Sugar**
A	1	3
B	2	3
C	1	4
D	2	4

CAS KA1.1 Page 8

HTP Page 1

aKU

C

2 The table below shows the effects on the lengths of three 100 mm potato tissue strips after each was immersed in a solution of different solute concentrations for one hour.

Solution	Length of potato strip after one hour of immersion (mm)
X	100
Y	96
Z	106

Which of the following conclusions is valid?

A Solution Z had a higher solute concentration than solution X.
B Solution Y was of the same solute concentration as the potato cell sap.
C Solution Z had a higher solute concentration than solution Y.
D Solution Y had a higher solute concentration than the potato cell sap.

CAS KA1.2 Page 8

HTP Pages 145 and 147

Concluding

A

3 The information encoded into DNA determines the structure and function of

A bases
B proteins
C amino acids
D carbohydrates.

4 The apparatus shown below was set up and left for 24 hours.

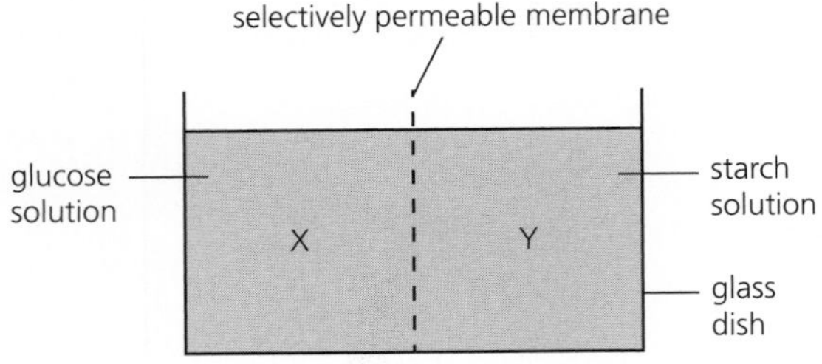

Which line in the table below shows the substances that would be present in regions X and Y after 24 hours?

	Substances present	
	Region X	**Region Y**
A	glucose only	glucose and starch
B	glucose only	starch only
C	glucose and starch	glucose and starch
D	glucose and starch	starch only

5 Which line in the table below gives a requirement and a product of aerobic respiration in mammalian muscle cells?

	Requirement	Product
A	oxygen	water
B	carbon dioxide	water
C	oxygen	lactic acid
D	carbon dioxide	lactic acid

STUDENT MARGIN

CAS KA1.4, P 9
HTP, P 16
dKU; **C**

CAS KA1.2 Page 8
HTP Pages 5 and 146
Predicting
C

CAS KA1.8 Page 10
HTP Page 32
dKU
C

6 Four test-tubes were set up as shown below.

1 cm^3 of yeast suspended in distilled water was added to each tube and left for 24 hours.

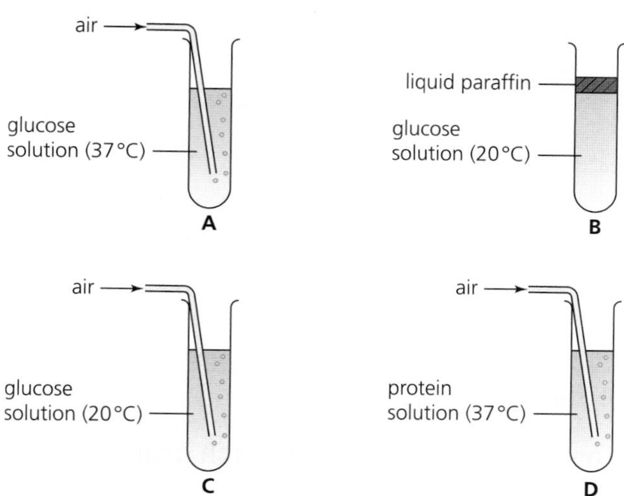

In which tube would the greatest concentration of ethanol be found after 24 hours?

STUDENT MARGIN

CAS KA1.8 Page 10

HTP Page 32

aKU

C

7 The following list shows steps in the process of genetic engineering.

1 Required gene inserted into vector.
2 Gene extracted from source chromosome.
3 Section of DNA with required gene identified.
4 Vector inserted into host cell.

In which order would these steps normally occur?

A 2, 3, 4, 1
B 2, 3, 1, 4
C 3, 2, 4, 1
D 3, 2, 1, 4

CAS KA1.6 Page 9

HTP Page 23

dKU

C

8 Which line in the table below gives characteristics of human stem cells?

	Characteristic	
	Chromosome number	**Potential for cell division**
A	haploid	cannot divide
B	haploid	can divide
C	diploid	cannot divide
D	diploid	can divide

CAS KA2.2 Page 10

HTP Page 51

dKU

C

9 The diagram below shows the structure of a flower.

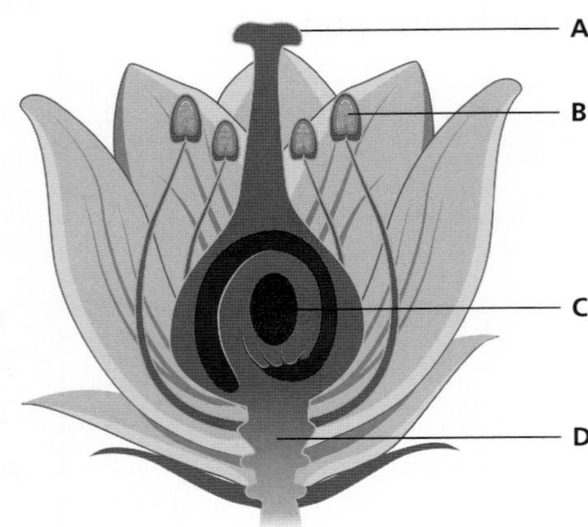

Which structure is the site of production of female gametes?

CAS **KA2.4** Page 11
HTP Page 63
aKU
C

10 In maize, purple grain colour **P** is dominant to yellow grain colour **p**. Each grain of a maize cob is formed from a separate fertilisation.

The diagram below shows a cross between two maize plants and a cob from one of the F_1 offspring. The number of purple and yellow grains on the cob is also shown.

Parents maize plant X maize plant

F_1 offspring

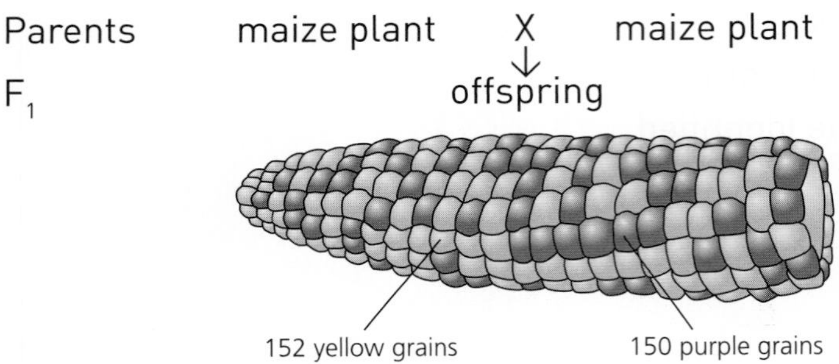

The genotypes of the parents that produced the F_1 offspring from which this cob was taken were

A PP and pp
B Pp and pp
C both Pp
D both pp.

STUDENT MARGIN

CAS **KA2.5** Page 11
HTP Page 66
aKU
A

11 The diagram below shows a section through a human heart.

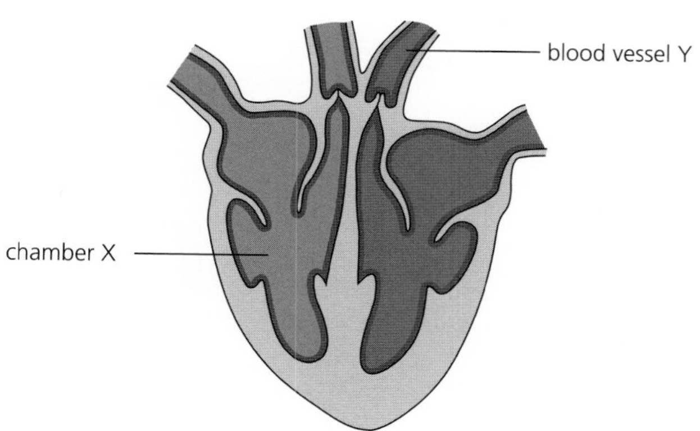

Which line in the table below identifies chamber X and the oxygen level of blood in vessel Y?

	Chamber X	Oxygen level of blood in vessel Y
A	right ventricle	low
B	left ventricle	low
C	left ventricle	high
D	right ventricle	high

12 Which line in the table describes features of active transport through cell membranes?

	Feature of active transport	
	Membrane component involved	**Direction of movement of molecules on the concentration gradient**
A	phospholipid	down
B	protein	against
C	phospholipid	against
D	protein	down

13 In an investigation, the effects of the sugar concentration in drinks on the volume of urine produced by participants was measured.

Which variable should be kept constant during this investigation?

A volume of drink given
B volume of urine measured
C concentration of sugars in drinks
D concentration of urine measured

STUDENT MARGIN

CAS KA2.6 Page 11
HTP Page 74
aKU
C

CAS KA1.2 Page 8
HTP Page 5
dKU
C

CAS KA2.7 Page 12
HTP Pages 135 and 145
Planning
A

14 The diagram below shows organs in the human abdomen.

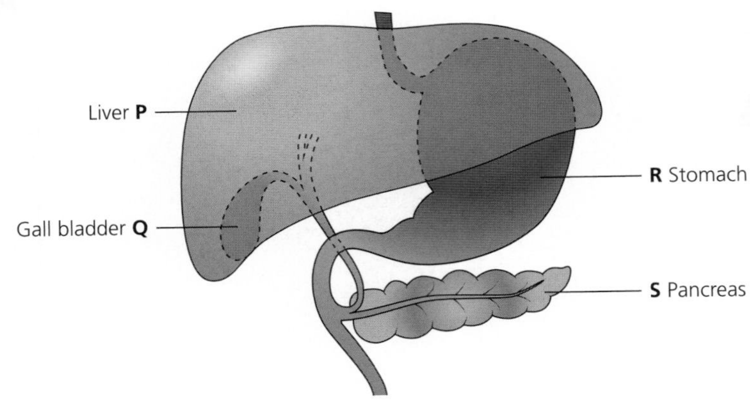

Which line in the table below identifies the organs that contain cells that synthesise the substances shown?

	Substances synthesised	
	glycogen	**glucagon**
A	P	S
B	R	S
C	P	Q
D	R	Q

STUDENT MARGIN

CAS KA2.3 Page 11

HTP Page 60

aKU

A

15 Which of the following best describes an ecosystem?

A a region of the planet with its own climate, fauna and flora
B a habitat with its living community and its non-living parts
C the biotic and abiotic factors affecting a habitat
D the role an organism plays within its community

CAS KA3.1, P 12

HTP, P 97

dKU

C

16 The following list shows events that were observed after the accidental release of fertiliser into a freshwater loch located in an agricultural area in lowland Scotland.

1 death of algae and larger water plants
2 algal bloom in loch water
3 increase in bacterial numbers in water samples
4 reduction in dissolved oxygen in water samples

Following release of the fertiliser, in which order would these events be expected to happen?

A 2, 1, 3, 4
B 3, 2, 1, 4
C 4, 2, 3, 1
D 2, 3, 4, 1

CAS KA3.5 Page 13

HTP Page 119

aKU

A

17 Speciation is said to have occurred when

A selection pressures result in survival of the fittest variants
B isolation divides a population into two different sub-populations
C breeding between two sub-populations fails to produce fertile offspring
D mutations produce significant differences between members of a population.

18 Bacteria living in the root nodules of pea plants are beneficial to the plant because they convert

A nitrites to nitrates
B ammonia to nitrites
C nitrogen to nitrates
D ammonia to nitrogen.

19 Mayflies are indicators of unpolluted water. The table below shows the average masses of mayflies in samples taken from a Scottish river over a period of months.

Month	Average mass of mayflies in sample (g)
January	30
February	40
March	48
April	50
May	55
June	60

What was the percentage increase in average mass of mayflies in the samples between January and June?

A 30
B 50
C 60
D 100

STUDENT MARGIN

CAS **KA3.4**, P 13
HTP, P 114
dKU; **C**

CAS **KA3.2**, P 12
HTP, P 102
dKU; **C**

CAS **KA3.5** Page 13
HTP Pages 134 and 146
Processing
C

20 The chart shows the yields of raw sugar from two African varieties of sugar cane from three sample plots in a sugar plantation.

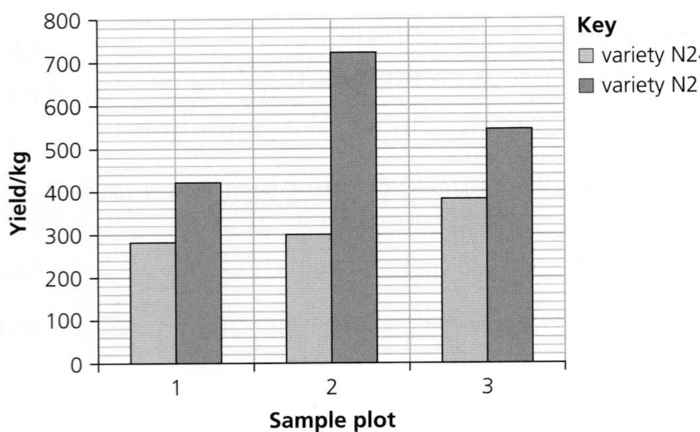

What was the average yield of sugar from variety N24 from the sample plots?

A 280
B 320
C 560
D 840

STUDENT MARGIN

CAS
KA2.5
Page 11

HTP
Pages 133 and 146

Selecting

C

[End of Section 1 — Answers on pages 81–82]

[Now attempt the questions in Section 2]

Section 2

SECTION 2 — 60 marks

Attempt ALL questions in this section.

Write your answers clearly in the spaces provided in this paper. Additional space for answers and rough work is provided at the end of this paper. If you use this space you must clearly identify the question number you are attempting. Any rough work must be written in this space. You should score through your rough work when you have written your final copy.

Use **blue** or **black** ink.

		MARKS	STUDENT MARGIN
1	The diagram below represents a bacterial cell. X ribosomes cell wall circular chromosome		**CAS KA1.1** Page 8 **HTP** Page 1
a)	Name structure X. __________	1	aKU **C**
b)	Give the function of ribosomes. __________	1	dKU **C**
c)	Describe how the cell wall of this cell may differ from the cell wall of a plant cell. __________ __________	1	dKU **C**
d)	Describe the organisation of DNA molecules within a bacterial cell. __________ __________ __________	2	dKU **CA**

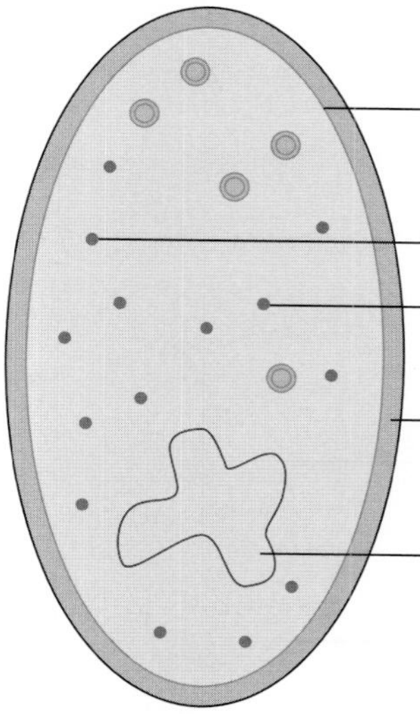

[Model answers on page 83]

A

		MARKS	STUDENT MARGIN
2	The diagrams below represent three consecutive stages in the process of mitosis in an animal cell.		**CAS KA1.3** Page 9 **HTP** Page 12

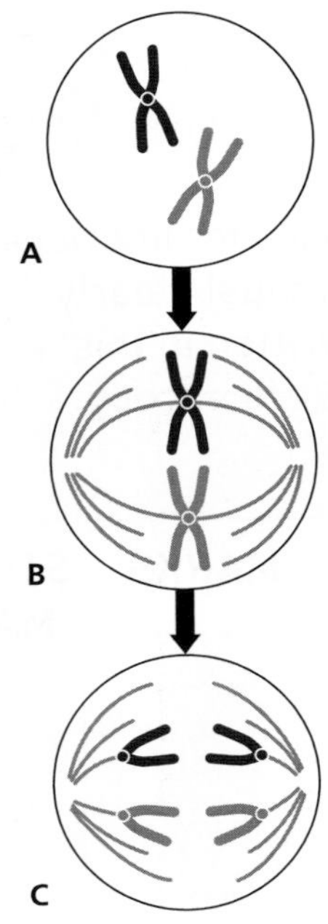

a) Describe the changes that have occurred

(i) between stages A and B — 2 — aKU **CA**

____

____

____

(ii) between stages B and C. — 1 — aKU **C**

____

____

b) State why mitosis is required in the bodies of multicellular animals. — 1 — dKU **C**

____

[Model answers on page 83]

		MARKS	STUDENT MARGIN
3	**a)** The Human Genome Project (HGP) was started in 1987. Its goal was to map the human genes and sequence human DNA. Mapping would eventually reveal the position and spacing of the 100 000 genes that were thought at that time to be in each human body cell. Sequencing would determine the order of the base pairs that compose the DNA molecules. The primary motive was that which drives all basic science, namely, the need to know. The secondary motive was to identify the 4000 genes that were then suspected to be responsible for inherited diseases and prepare the way for treatment through gene therapy. This would benefit society because a library of DNA knowledge would jump-start medical research on many fronts. **Use the information from the passage above** to answer the following questions.		**CAS KA1.4** Page 9 **HTP** Pages 16, 133, 134 and 146
	(i) State one of the two main goals of HGP. ____________________ ____________________	1	Selecting **CC**
	(ii) Give the purpose of carrying out DNA mapping ____________________ ____________________	1	
	(iii) Calculate the percentage of the human genes that were suspected of being responsible for inherited disease in 1987. *Space for calculation* ____________%	1	Processing **C**
	(iv) State why it was thought that knowledge of the human genome could benefit society. ____________________ ____________________	1	Selecting **A**
	(v) Identify a phrase, mentioned in the passage, which suggests that opinion about the number of genes in the human genome has changed since the HGP began. ____________________ ____________________	1	Selecting **A**
	b) Give the name of one of the base pairs found in DNA. __________ and __________	1	dKU **C**

[Model answers on pages 83–4]

MARKS STUDENT MARGIN

4 An experiment was carried out to investigate how temperature affected the rate of breakdown of starch by an enzyme in human saliva. In this experiment, 50 mg of starch suspended in 100 cm^3 of distilled water was mixed with 10 cm^3 of saliva solution and the mass of starch broken down in one hour was measured. The procedure was repeated at a range of temperatures.

CAS KA1.5 Page 9

HTP Pages 19, 134, 135, 145, 146 and 147

The table below shows the results.

Temperature (°C)	Mass of starch broken down in one hour (mg)
10	6
20	12
30	19
40	21
50	18
60	0

a) On the grid, complete the vertical axis and plot a line graph of the temperature against the mass of starch broken down in one hour. (Additional graph paper, if required, can be found on page 26.) 2

Presenting

CC

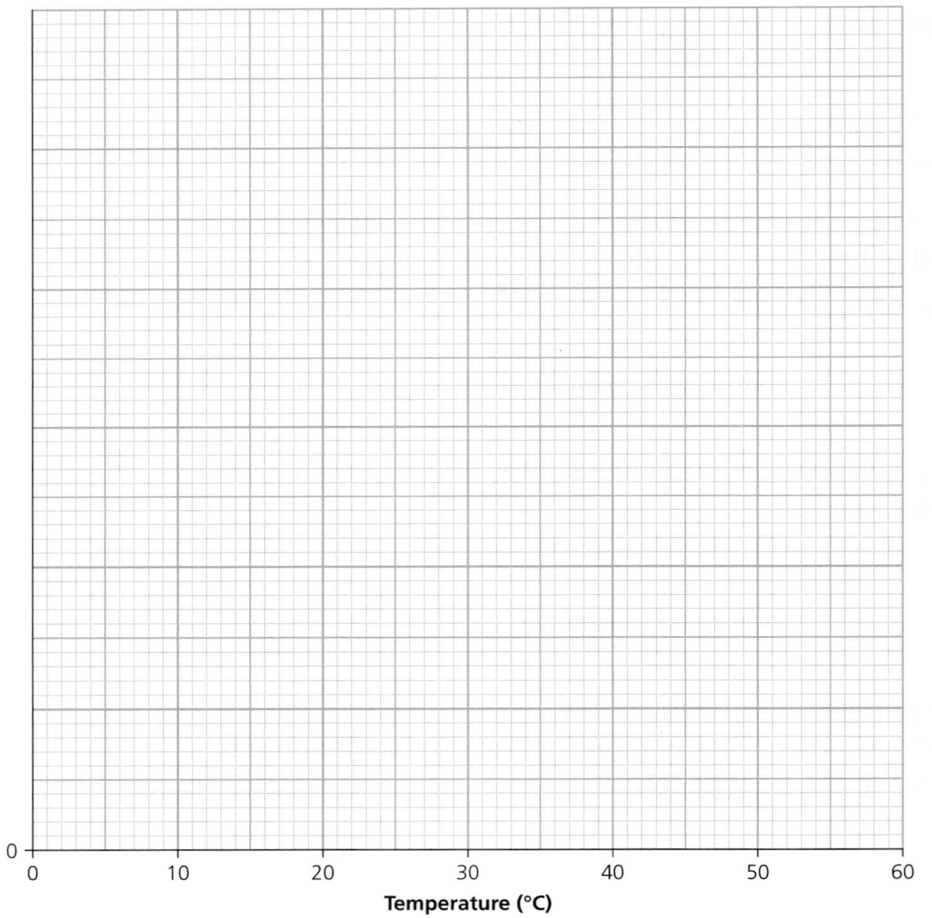

	MARKS	STUDENT MARGIN
b) Calculate the mass of starch that would be broken down by this enzyme in **three** hours at 25 °C. *Space for calculation* ______ mg	1	Processing **C**
c) **(i)** Suggest an improvement to the experiment that would increase the reliability of the results obtained. ______ ______	1	Planning **C**
(ii) The investigators concluded that the optimum temperature of the enzyme was 40 °C. Describe evidence from the data that might suggest that this is not accurate. ______ ______ ______	1	Evaluating **A**
d) The active enzyme in human saliva is amylase which has starch as its substrate. Name another example of an enzyme and its substrate. Name ______ Substrate ______	1	dKU **C**

[Model answers on page 84]

MARKS | STUDENT MARGIN

5 a) The diagram below represents a section through part of a leaf.

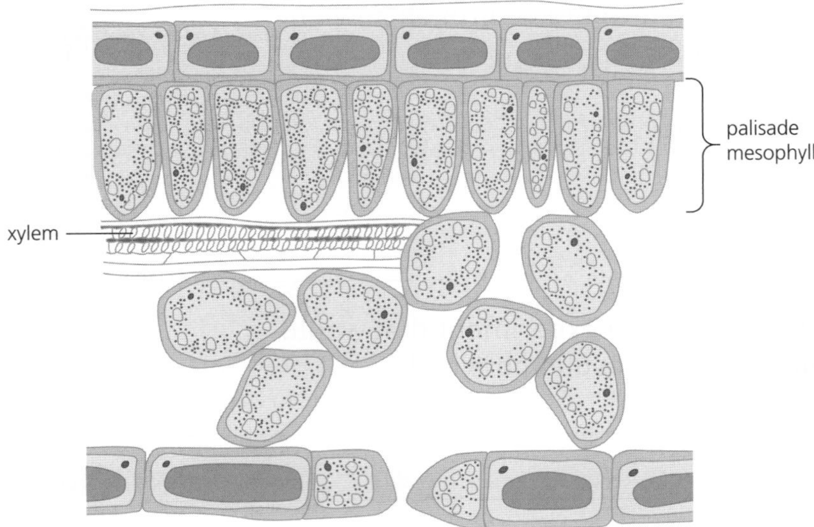

CAS **KA2.6** Page 11

HTP Pages 71 and 147

(i) Give **one** feature of palisade mesophyll tissue that allows it to carry out the process of photosynthesis efficiently. 1 aKU **A**

____

____

(ii) **Add arrows to the diagram** to show the pathway taken by water as it moves from the xylem to the atmosphere surrounding the leaf. 1 aKU **C**

(iii) Name the substance that forms the supportive rings and spirals shown in the xylem in the diagram. 1 dKU **C**

____

b) The table below shows information about the distribution of stomata in the leaves of various food plant species.

Food plant species	Number of stomata per cm² of leaf surface	
	Upper epidermis	Lower epidermis
bean	4000	25 000
maize	6000	10 000
orange tree	none	45 000
sunflower	9000	16 000
apple tree	none	39 000

Give **two** conclusions that could be drawn from the data in the table. 2 Concluding **CA**

1 ____

____

2 ____

____

[Model answers on pages 84–5]

	MARKS	STUDENT MARGIN

6 The rate of photosynthesis can be estimated by measuring the rate at which bubbles of oxygen gas are given off from the cut end of a pondweed stem.

The graph below shows the rate of photosynthesis when a stem of a water plant was kept at various combinations of temperatures and carbon dioxide concentrations and exposed to different light intensities.

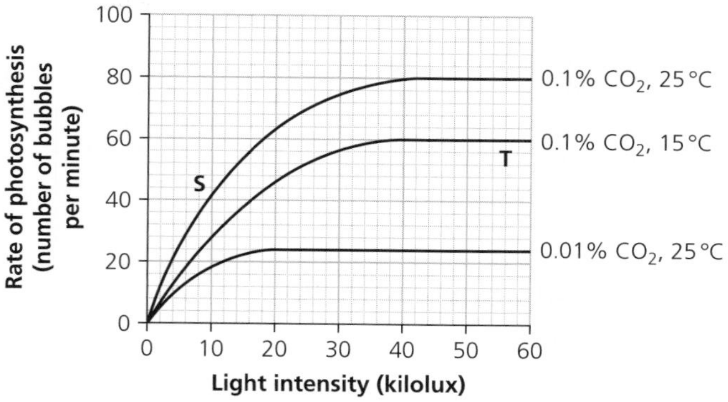

CAS KA1.7 Page 9

HTP Pages 27, 134 and 146

a) (i) Calculate the simplest whole number ratio of bubbles produced at 15 °C compared with 25 °C when the light intensity was 50 kilolux and the CO_2 level was 0.1%. **1**

Space for calculation

Processing **A**

__________ : __________

at 15 °C   at 25 °C

(ii) Name the factors that are most likely to be limiting the rate of photosynthesis at points S and T on the graph. **2**

aKU **AC**

S ____________________

T ____________________

b) (i) Apart from oxygen, name **one** product of photosynthesis. **1**

dKU **C**

____

(ii) Name the substance from which oxygen is released during photosynthesis. **1**

dKU **C**

____

[Model answers on page 85]

MARKS STUDENT MARGIN

7 a) The diagrams below represent two groups of cells from the epidermis of a plant.

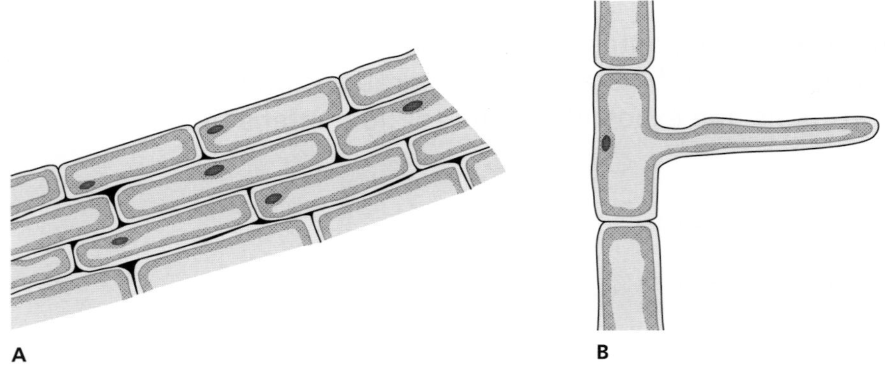

CAS KA2.1 Page 10

HTP Page 47

(i) Give the term used to describe groups of cells, such as these, which work together to carry out the same function. 1 dKU C

___

(ii) The epidermis in diagram B is highly specialised for its function. Suggest the location of this epidermis in the plant and describe how its structure is suited to its function. 2 aKU CA

Location ___

Description ___

___

b) The human body can be described as a group of body systems. Describe what is meant by a body system. 1 dKU C

___

___

[Model answers on page 85]

8 The diagram below represents a section through the human brain.

MARKS | STUDENT MARGIN

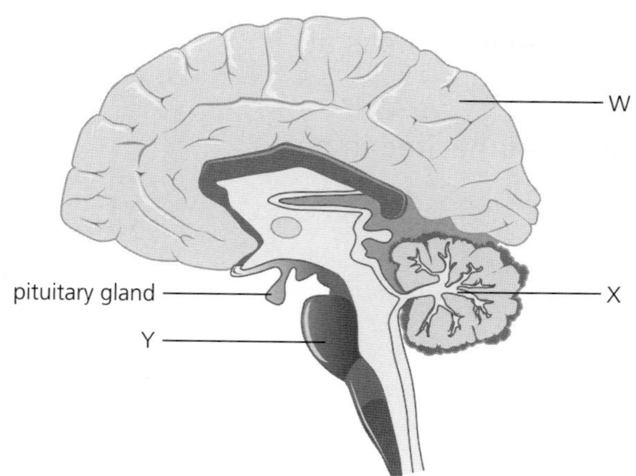

CAS KA2.3 Page 11

HTP Page 54

a) Complete the table below to name the parts of the brain labelled in the diagram and to give their functions. 2

Letter	Name of part	Function
W		controls reasoning and conscious thought
X	cerebellum	
Y		controls breathing rate and peristalsis

dKU

CC

b) The pituitary gland releases specific hormones that can affect only their target tissues and no others.

Explain how a hormone can affect its target tissues but not others. 1

____

____

aKU

A

[Model answers on page 85]

	MARKS	STUDENT MARGIN

9 The ability to taste the substance phenylthiocarbamide (PTC) is inherited. Individuals are either tasters and identify the substance by its very bitter taste or non-tasters who do not taste the bitterness at all. **T** is the allele for tasting and **t** for non-tasting.

The diagram below shows how the characteristic was inherited in part of a family tree.

CAS KA2.5 Page 11

HTP Pages 66 and 146

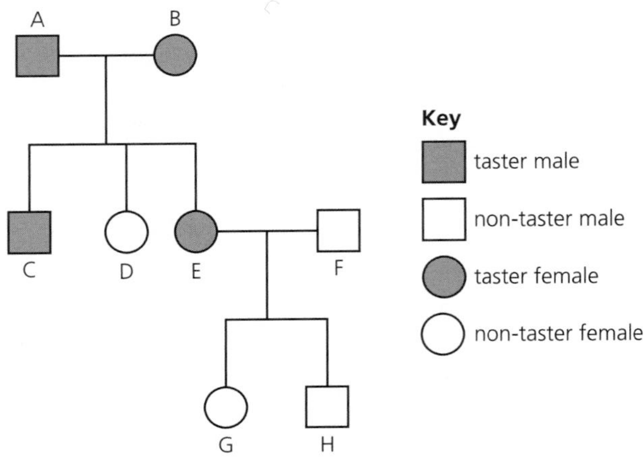

a) Describe **one** piece of evidence from the family tree that can confirm that the non-taster allele is recessive. 1 — aKU **A**

____

____

b) State the phenotype of person C. 1 — aKU **C**

____

c) Person H marries a woman who is a non-taster.

Predict the percentage chance that their first child will be able to taste PTC. 1 — Predicting **A**

Space for calculation

______________ %

d) Identify the type of variation shown by this example. 1 — aKU **C**

____

[Model answers on pages 85–6]

10 Oxygen levels in the atmosphere decrease with altitude. The red blood cell counts of members of a 100-day climbing expedition were investigated. **Graph 1** shows the altitudes at which camps were set up each night and **Graph 2** shows the average red blood cell count of the mountaineers over the expedition period.

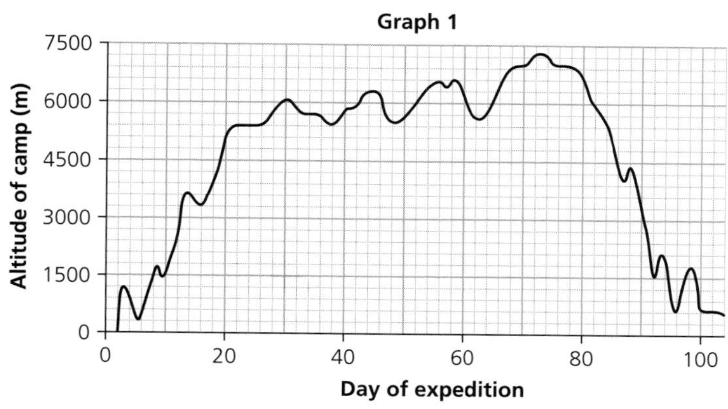

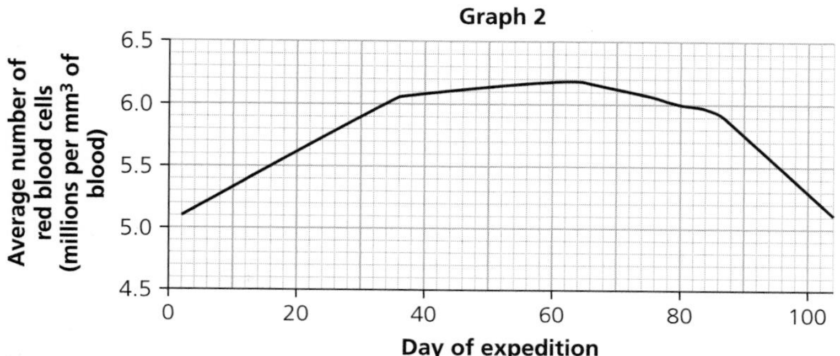

CAS KA2.6 Page 11

HTP Pages 74, 133, 134, 146, 147

a) **(i)** Give **one** general conclusion that can be made from the data shown in the graphs. — 1 — Concluding **C**

____

____

(ii) Give the day of the expedition on which the average red blood cell count of the climbers first reached 6 million cells per mm^3. — 1 — Selecting **A**

____

(iii) Calculate the **range** of average red blood cell count over the 100 days. — 1 — Processing **C**

Space for calculation

________________ cells per mm^3

			MARKS	STUDENT MARGIN
b)	(i)	Explain why it is an advantage to produce more red blood cells as altitude increases.	1	aKU **A**
	(ii)	Name the pigment found in red blood cells.	1	dKU **C**

[Model answers on page 86]

MARKS | STUDENT MARGIN

11 Give an account of different types of competition in ecosystems. 4

CAS
KA3.2
Page 12

HTP
Page 102

dKU

CCCA

[Model answers on page 86]

MARKS | STUDENT MARGIN

12 The table below shows the average concentration of a pesticide in tissue samples at the different feeding levels in the food web of a freshwater ecosystem.

Feeding level	Average pesticide concentration in tissue samples (parts per million)
producer	0.05
primary consumer	0.3
secondary consumer	2.0
tertiary consumer	14.0

CAS KA3.5 Page 13
HTP Page 119

a) Explain how the pesticide might have entered the food web. 2

aKU CA

b) Explain the pattern of pesticide concentration increase through the feeding levels of this food web. 2

aKU CA

c) Biological control can be an alternative to the use of pesticides. State what is meant by the term biological control. 1

dKU C

[Model answers on pages 86–7]

13 a) The table below contains information about four species of coniferous tree from a Scottish woodland site. **MARKS** **STUDENT MARGIN**

Tree species	Colour of bark	Position of cones	Shape of needle tips
Picea abies	brown	hang down	pointed
Abies alba	grey	upright	notched
Abies procera	grey	upright	rounded
Picea sitchensis	grey	hang down	pointed

Using information from the table, complete the paired statement key below by filling in the missing information on the dotted lines. 2

CAS KA3.3 Page 16
HTP Pages 109 and 147
aKU
CA

1 Bark brown — *Picea abies*
Bark grey — go to 2

2 Cones upright — go to 3
Cones hang down — ……………

3 …………… — *Abies alba*
Needle tips rounded — ……………

b) Quadrats and pitfall traps are techniques that could be used to sample the organisms on a woodland floor.

Choose quadrat or pitfall trap and tick (✓) the appropriate box.

Quadrat ☐ Pitfall trap ☐

(i) Describe how the chosen sampling technique would be used. 1

dKU
C

___

___

(ii) Describe a source of error that could affect the results of sampling by this method. 1

Evaluating
C

___

___

[Model answers on page 87]

[END OF PRACTICE PAPER A]

ADDITIONAL SPACE FOR ANSWERS AND ROUGH WORK

ADDITIONAL GRAPH PAPER FOR QUESTION 4a)

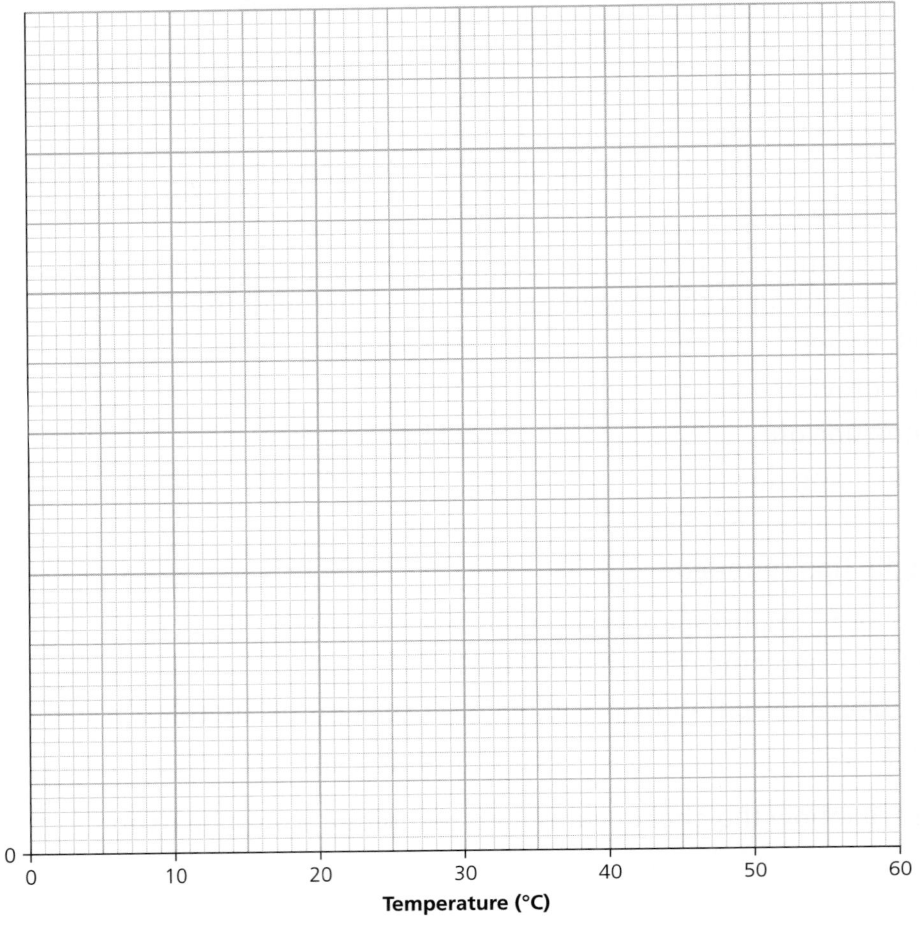

Practice Paper B

National 5 Biology

Section 1

SECTION 1 — 20 marks

Attempt ALL questions. Answer grid available at www.hoddereducation.co.uk/updatesandextras.

STUDENT MARGIN

1 Plant cell walls are composed mainly of

A phospholipid
B protein
C cellulose
D starch.

CAS KA1.1, P 8 **HTP**, P 1 dKU; **C**

2 Which of the following cells do **not** contain organelles?

A bacterial
B animal
C plant
D fungal

CAS KA1.1, P 8 **HTP**, P 1 dKU; **C**

3 Which line in the table below describes the cells produced after mitosis?

	Cells produced after mitosis	
	Chromosome complement	**Genetic composition**
A	haploid	all cells different
B	diploid	all cells identical
C	diploid	all cells different
D	haploid	all cells identical

CAS KA1.3 Page 9 **HTP** Page 12 dKU **C**

4 The table below shows the number of bacterial colonies counted on four different agar plates.

Agar plate	Number of bacterial colonies
P	250
Q	216
R	216
S	194

The average number of bacterial colonies on these plates was

A 216
B 219
C 438
D 876

CAS KA1.3 Page 9 **HTP** Pages 134 and 146 Processing **C**

STUDENT MARGIN

5 Enzymes are proteins and are composed of

A bases
B genes
C DNA
D amino acids.

CAS KA1.5, P 9
HTP, P 19
dKU; **C**

6 Which of the following products from the light reactions of photosynthesis are required for the carbon fixation stage?

A ATP and hydrogen
B water and carbon dioxide
C ATP and water
D hydrogen and carbon dioxide

CAS KA1.7, P 9
HTP, P 27
aKU
C

7 Which line in the table correctly shows chemical reactions that take place during aerobic respiration?

	Chemical reaction 1	Chemical reaction 2
A	ADP + Pi → ATP	pyruvate → lactic acid
B	ATP → ADP + Pi	pyruvate → lactic acid
C	ADP + Pi → ATP	pyruvate → carbon dioxide + water
D	ATP → ADP + Pi	pyruvate → carbon dioxide + ethanol

CAS KA1.8 Page 10
HTP Page 32
dKU
C

8 The effect of light intensity on the rate of photosynthesis at different temperatures is shown in the graph.

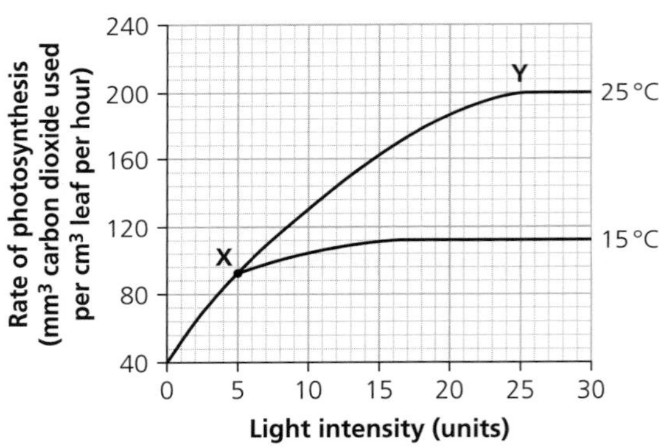

Which of the following conclusions can be made **from the information given** in the graph?

A At point Y, the rate of photosynthesis is limited by the light intensity.
B Temperature only affects the rate of photosynthesis at light intensities greater than 15 units.
C At point Y, temperature is the limiting factor.
D At point X, light intensity and temperature limit the rate of photosynthesis.

CAS KA1.7 Page 9
HTP Pages 133 and 146
Concluding
A

9 The diagram below shows four different specialised cells.

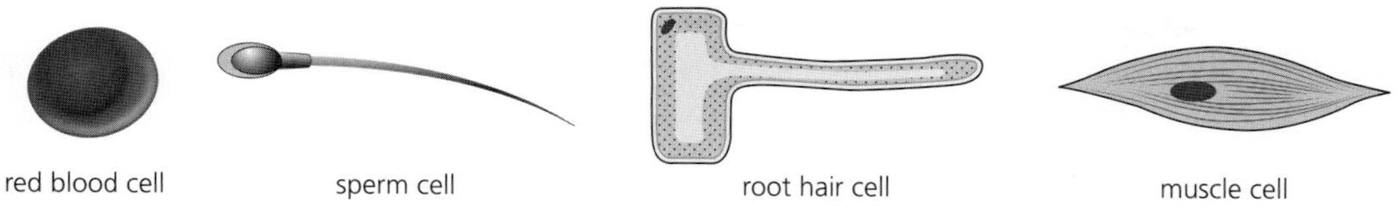

Which cell is specialised to increase the surface area available for the absorption of water?

A red blood cell
B sperm cell
C root hair cell
D muscle cell

10 The diagram below shows cells in a section through a leaf.

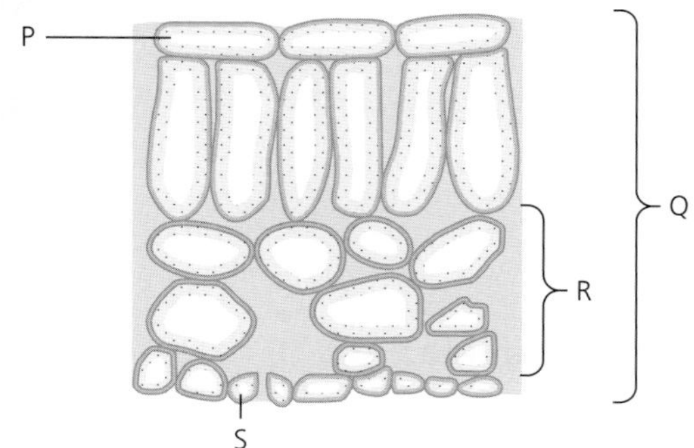

Which line in the table below correctly identifies a tissue and an organ?

	Tissue	Organ
A	S	P
B	R	Q
C	R	S
D	Q	S

11 The following stages occur in a reflex action.

1 An impulse passes along a sensory neuron.
2 A sense organ detects a stimulus.
3 The effector produces a response.
4 An impulse passes along a motor neuron.

The correct order of the stages is

A 2, 1, 4, 3
B 2, 4, 1, 3
C 3, 1, 4, 2
D 1, 2, 4, 3

STUDENT MARGIN

CAS KA2.1 Page 10
HTP Page 47
aKU
C

CAS KA2.1 Page10
HTP Page 47
aKU
C

CAS KA2.3 Page 11
HTP Page 54
dKU
C

12 The diagram below shows a section through the human brain.

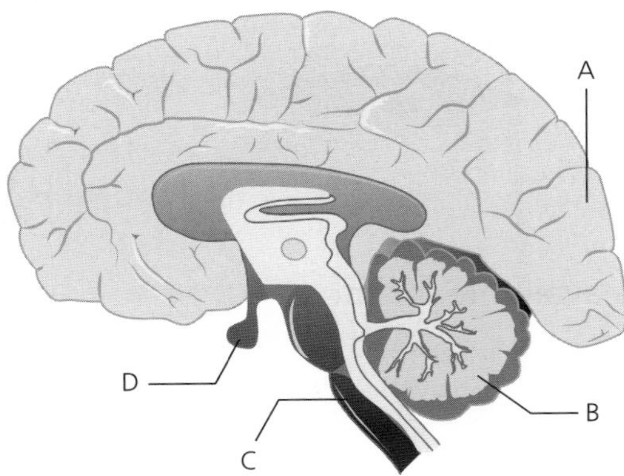

Which letter indicates the site of the centre for control of breathing?

STUDENT MARGIN

CAS KA2.3 Page 11
HTP Page 54
dKU
C

13 A characteristic with a range of variation between two extremes is described as

A a recessive characteristic
B a dominant characteristic
C showing discrete variation
D showing continuous variation.

CAS KA2.5 Page 11
HTP Page 66
dKU
C

14 Cystic fibrosis is an inherited condition caused by a recessive allele.

The diagram below is a pedigree chart showing the inheritance of this condition in a family.

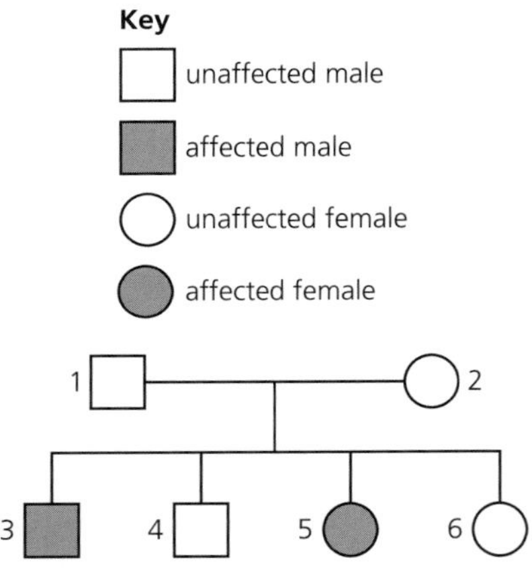

Which two individuals in the pedigree chart **must** be heterozygous for the cystic fibrosis allele?

A 1 and 2
B 3 and 5
C 4 and 6
D 2 and 6

CAS KA2.5 Page 11
HTP Page 66
aKU
A

STUDENT MARGIN

15 The table below shows the responses of a group of 120 Scottish students when asked about their smoking habits.

	Smoking habits			
	Never smoked	**Tried smoking**	**Occasional smoker**	**Regular smoker**
Student response (%)	12.5	50	12.5	25

How many students in the sample said they were occasional smokers?

A 12.5
B 15
C 60
D 96

CAS KA2.7 Page 12
HTP Pages 134 and 146
Processing
A

16 A 30 g bowl of breakfast cereal contains 1.5 mg of iron. Only 25% of this iron is absorbed into the bloodstream.

If a pregnant woman requires 6 mg of iron per day, how much cereal would be needed to provide this?

A 60 g
B 120 g
C 240 g
D 480 g

CAS KA2.7 Page 12
HTP Pages 134 and 146
Processing
A

17 Which of the graphs below shows the most likely result of the effect of interspecific competition between species X and species Y for the same food source in a laboratory experiment?

Graph A

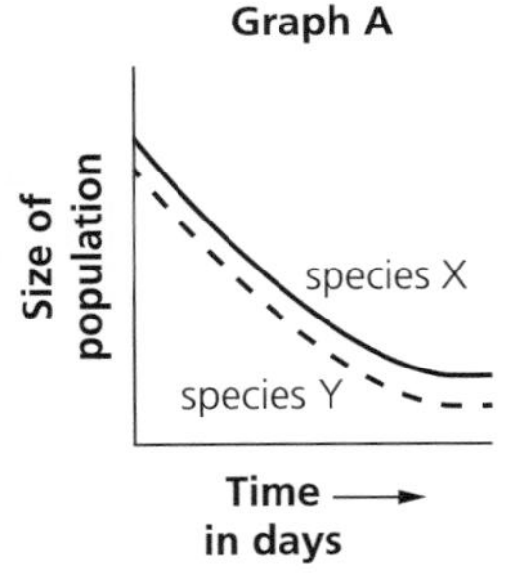

Graph B

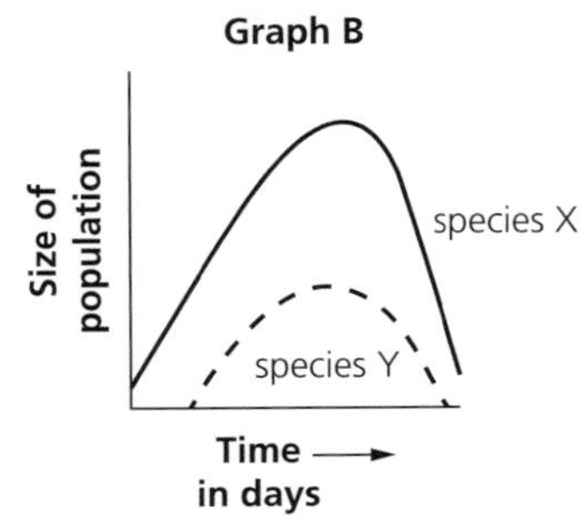

Graph C

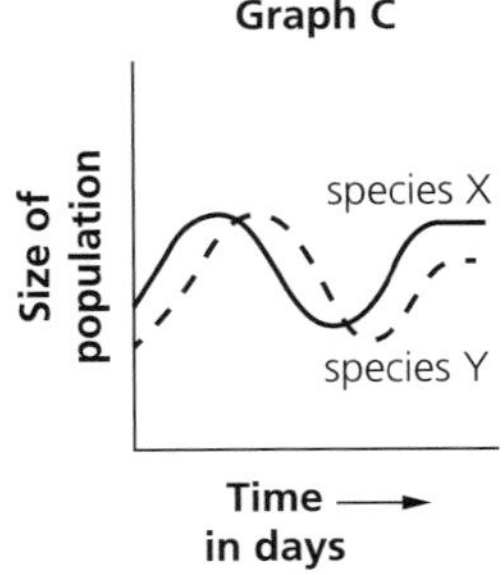

Graph D

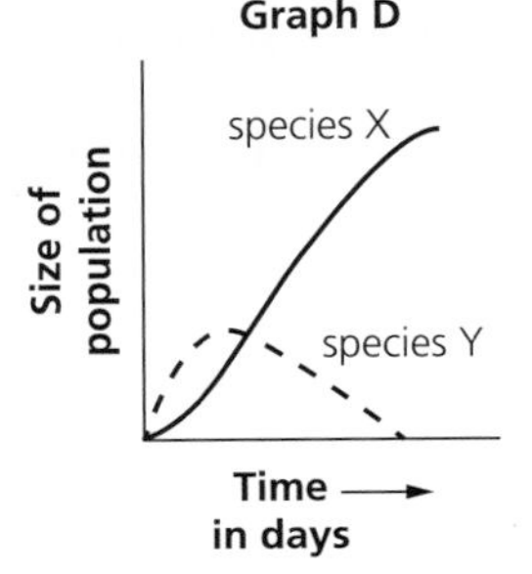

CAS KA3.2 Page 12
HTP Page 102
aKU
A

18 A single oak tree provides all the food for a large population of caterpillars, which are a prey species for several small birds. The small birds are eaten by a bird of prey.

Which of the pyramids of numbers shown below correctly represents this food chain?

STUDENT MARGIN

CAS KA3.2 Page 12
HTP Page 102
aKU
A

19 An investigation into competition between invertebrates in moist leaf litter was carried out.

Which line in the table below shows the type of factor under investigation and an appropriate method of sampling the organisms?

	Type of factor	Sampling method
A	biotic	quadrat
B	abiotic	quadrat
C	biotic	pitfall trap
D	abiotic	pitfall trap

CAS KA3.3 Page 13
HTP Page 109
aKU
C

20 Which line in the table below correctly shows characteristics of mutant alleles?

	Frequency	Occurrence
A	low	random
B	low	non-random
C	high	random
D	high	non-random

CAS KA3.4 Page 13
HTP Page 114
dKU
C

[End of Section 1 — Answers on pages 88–9]

[Now attempt the questions in Section 2]

Section 2

SECTION 2 — 60 marks

Attempt ALL questions in this section.

Write your answers clearly in the spaces provided in this paper. Additional space for answers and rough work is provided at the end of this paper. If you use this space you must clearly identify the question number you are attempting. Any rough work must be written in this space. You should score through your rough work when you have written your final copy.

Use **blue** or **black** ink.

MARKS | **STUDENT MARGIN**

1 The diagram below shows a liver cell and a magnified section of its cell membrane.

CAS KA1.2 Page 8
HTP Page 5

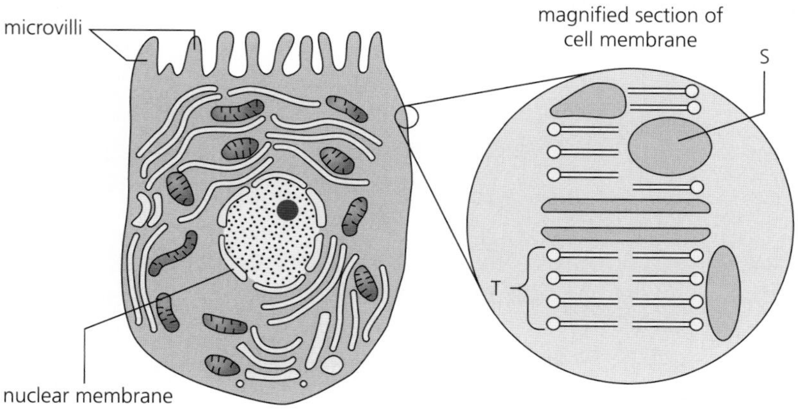

a) Name the two chemical components of the cell membrane labelled S and T. — 2 — dKU **C**

S ________________________________

T ________________________________

b) Glucose can be taken up by the liver cells by the process of diffusion.

(i) Describe the process of diffusion. — 1 — dKU **C**

____

____

(ii) Explain how the microvilli increase the rate of uptake of glucose into the liver cell. — 1 — aKU **A**

____

____

c) Explain the importance of diffusion to active cells such as liver cells. — 1 — aKU **A**

____

____

[Model answers on page 90]

MARKS | STUDENT MARGIN

2 a) Decide if each of the statements relating to DNA in the table below is **true** or **false** and tick (✓) the appropriate box. 3

If you decide the statement is **false**, write the correct term in the correction box to replace the term underlined in the statement.

Statement	True	False	Correction
DNA carries the genetic information, which is information for making amino acids.			
The four bases in DNA are adenine (A), thymine (T), cytosine (C) and guanine (G).			
The synthesis of mRNA takes place in the nucleus.			

CAS KA 1.4 Page 9

HTP Pages 16, 134 and 146

dKU

CCA

b) If a DNA molecule contains 2000 bases of which 20% are adenine, calculate the number of guanine bases that it would contain. 1

Space for calculation

Processing

A

________________ bases

c) Name the cell structure(s) where protein is assembled from amino acids. 1

dKU

C

____

[Model answers on page 90]

3 Genetic information can be transferred between cells or species, naturally or by genetic engineering.

	MARKS	STUDENT MARGIN
a) State **one** way in which DNA can be transferred naturally between cells. ____________________	1	**CAS** **KA1.6**, P 9 **HTP**, P 23 dKU; **A**
b) Genetic engineering uses bacteria to produce human insulin. Describe the stages involved in this process. Labelled diagrams may be included where appropriate.	4	dKU **CCCA**

Space for diagrams

[Model answers on pages 90–1]

MARKS STUDENT MARGIN

4 The rate of respiration in living tissue is measured using a device called a respirometer. The diagram below shows the apparatus used in an investigation of aerobic respiration in snails.

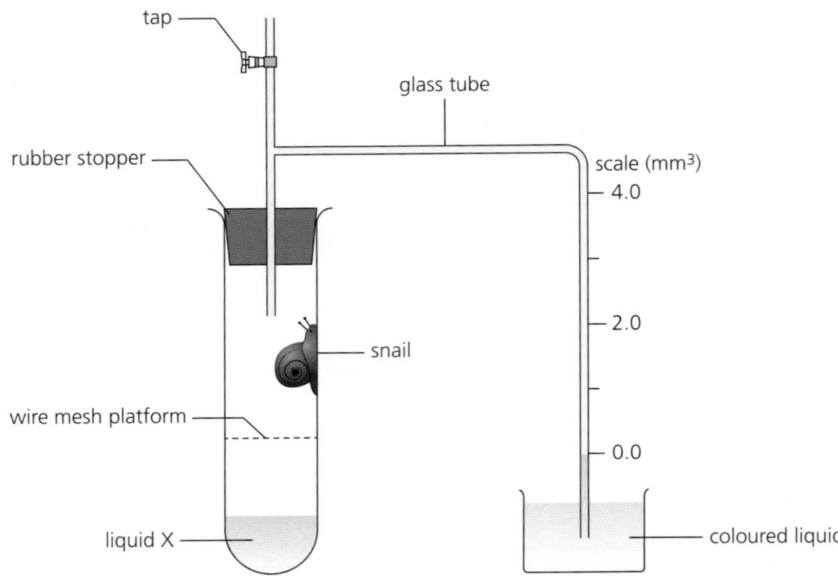

The reading on the scale was recorded every 2 minutes over a 10-minute period. The table below shows the results.

Time after tap closed (minutes)	Reading on scale (mm^3)
0	0.0
2	0.4
4	0.8
6	1.2
8	1.6
10	2.0

a) On the grid on page 39, draw a line graph of the time after the tap was closed against the reading on the scale. 2
(Additional graph paper, if required, can be found on page 49.)

CAS KA1.8 Page 10

HTP Pages 32, 134, 135, 145 and 146

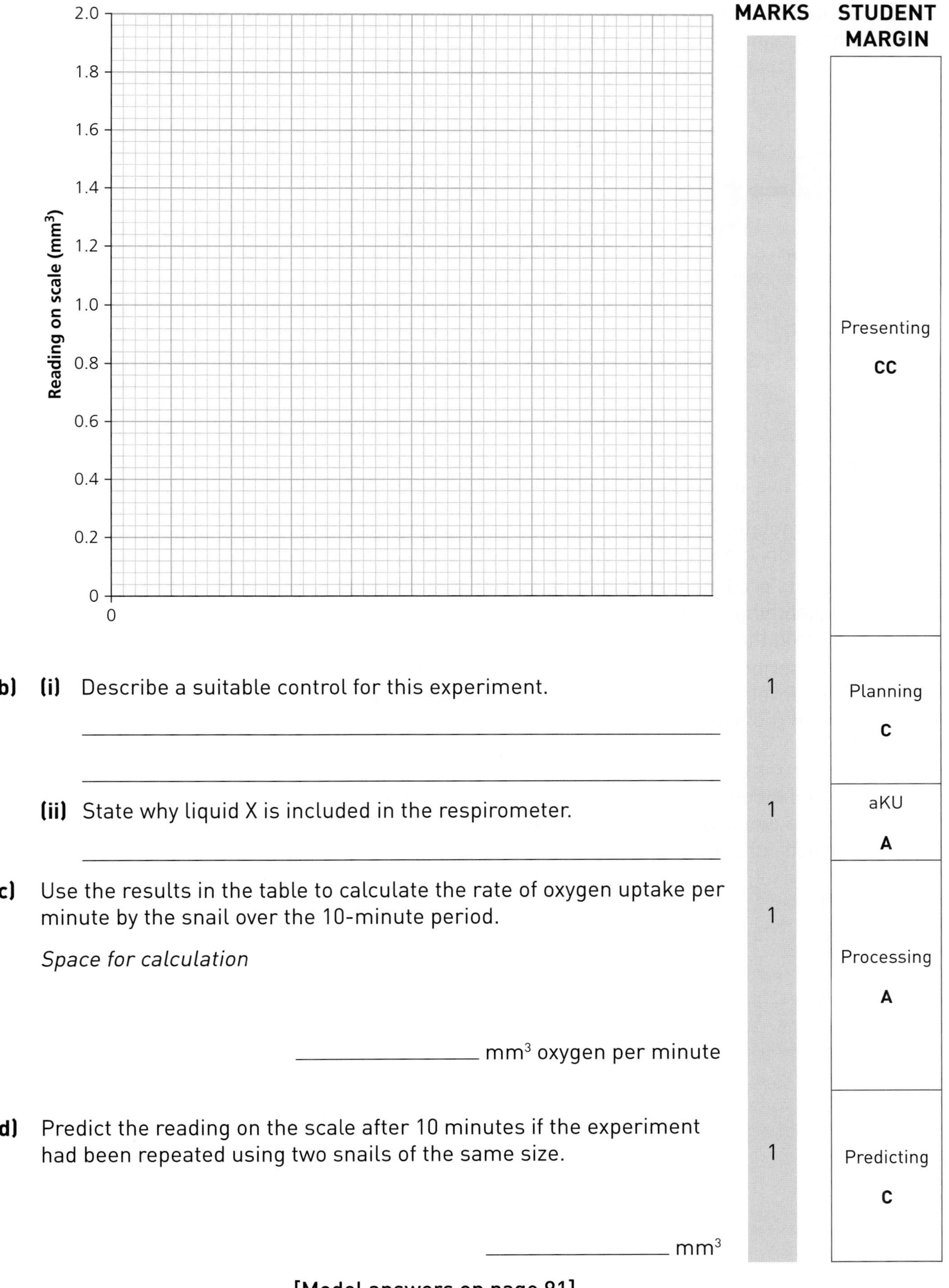

MARKS | STUDENT MARGIN

Presenting CC

b) **(i)** Describe a suitable control for this experiment. 1 — Planning C

____

____

(ii) State why liquid X is included in the respirometer. 1 — aKU A

____

c) Use the results in the table to calculate the rate of oxygen uptake per minute by the snail over the 10-minute period. 1 — Processing A

Space for calculation

________________ mm^3 oxygen per minute

d) Predict the reading on the scale after 10 minutes if the experiment had been repeated using two snails of the same size. 1 — Predicting C

________________ mm^3

[Model answers on page 91]

MARKS | STUDENT MARGIN

5 The diagram below shows how cells from human embryos may be used to grow replacement body tissues.

CAS KA2.2 Page 10

HTP Page 51

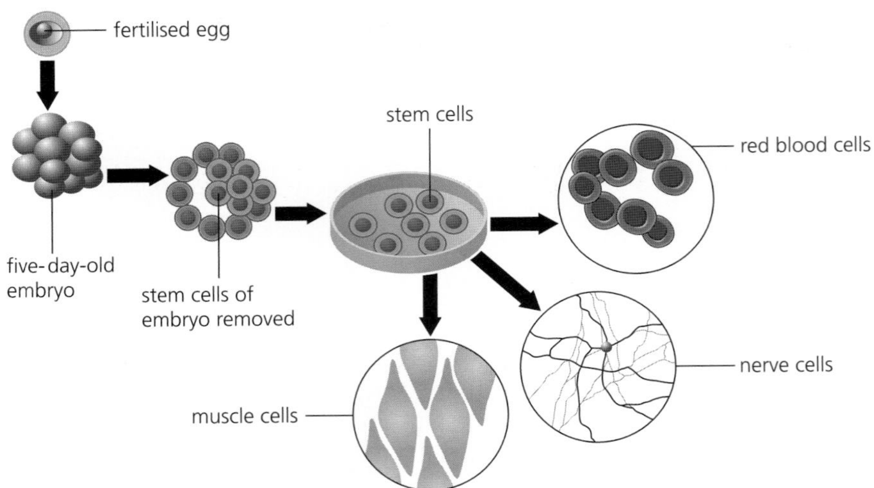

a) The fertilised egg undergoes mitosis and cell division to form the five-day-old embryo.

Complete the following sentences by underlining the correct option in each choice bracket. **2** dKU C

Cells produced by mitosis have (one matching set / two matching sets) of chromosomes, and are described as being (haploid / diploid).

b) Describe the feature of stem cells that gives them the potential to develop into many different types of cell, such as muscle, nerve and red blood cells. **1** dKU C

____

c) Red blood cells absorb and transport oxygen. Give two ways in which their structure is specialised to carry out their function. **2** dKU CC

1 ______________________________

____

2 ______________________________

____

[Model answers on pages 91–2]

		MARKS	STUDENT MARGIN

6 a) The control of blood glucose concentration carried out by the human liver is summarised in the diagram below.

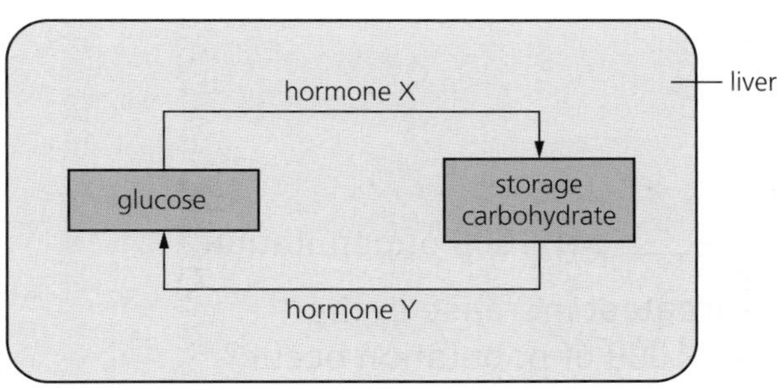

CAS KA2.3 Page 11

HTP Pages 60, 133, 134 and 146

(i) Excess blood glucose can be stored in the liver and muscles. Name the storage carbohydrate into which glucose is converted. **1**

dKU C

____

(ii) Name hormones X and Y. **2**

dKU CC

Hormone X ______________________________

Hormone Y ______________________________

b) The bar graph below shows the number of people with diabetes per 1000 of a human population.

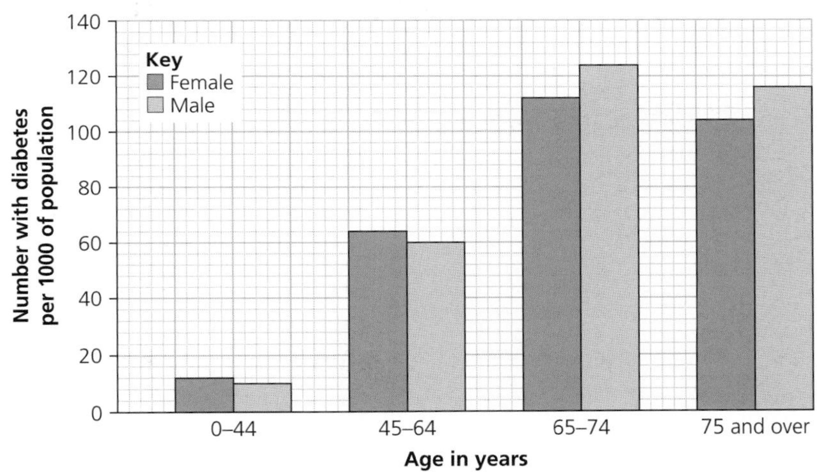

MARKS STUDENT MARGIN

(i) Calculate how many more males aged between 65 and 74 years of age have diabetes than males under 65 years of age. 1

Space for calculation

_______________ per 1000 of population

Processing A

(ii) Between which age ranges did the greatest increase in the number of females with diabetes per 1000 of population occur? 1

Tick (✓) the correct box.

☐	☐	☐
0–44 and 45–64	45–64 and 65–74	65–74 and 75 and over

Selecting C

[Model answers on page 92]

MARKS | STUDENT MARGIN

7 Give an account of fertilisation in either animals **or** flowering plants. Tick (✔) your choice. 3

Animals ☐ Plants ☐

CAS
KA2.4
Page 11

HTP
Page 63

dKU

CCA

[Model answers on page 92]

	MARKS	STUDENT MARGIN
8 In the fruit fly *Drosophila*, the allele for normal wings (**N**) is dominant to the allele for short wings (**n**).		**CAS KA2.5,** P 11 **HTP,** P 66
a) A male fly, homozygous for normal wings, was crossed with a female fly, homozygous for short wings.		
(i) Using the **letters** given complete the cross below to show the genotypes of the parents. P phenotype normal wing X short wing genotype ________ X ________	1	aKU **C**
(ii) Give the genotype of the F_1 offspring. F_1 genotype ________	1	aKU **C**
(iii) Describe the phenotype of the F_1 offspring. F_1 phenotype ________	1	aKU **C**
(iv) The F_1 offspring were allowed to mate with each other. Give the percentage of the F_2 offspring which would be expected to have normal wings. *Space for calculation* ________ %	1	aKU **C**
b) State what is meant by the term polygenic inheritance. ________ ________	1	dKU **C**

[Model answers on page 93]

9 a) The graph below shows the rate of water gain and water loss by a plant during a 24-hour period in summer.

MARKS	STUDENT MARGIN
	CAS KA2.6 Page 12 **HTP** Pages 71, 133, 134 and 146

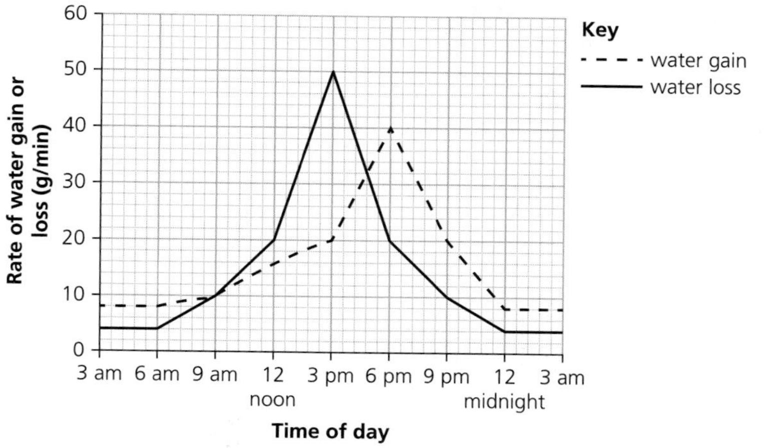

Rate of water gain or loss (g/min)

60, 50, 40, 30, 20, 10, 0

3 am, 6 am, 9 am, 12 noon, 3 pm, 6 pm, 9 pm, 12 midnight, 3 am

Time of day

Key

water gain (dashed line)

water loss (solid line)

(i) Use values from the graph to describe the rate of **water loss** by the plant over the 24-hour period. **2** — Selecting **CA**

____

____

____

____

____

____

(ii) Calculate the percentage increase in the **water gain** of the plant between 3 am and 9 pm. **1** — Processing **A**

Space for calculation

______________ %

(iii) Calculate, as the simplest whole number ratio, the water gain to water loss at 6 pm. **1** — Processing **C**

Space for calculation

______________ : ______________

water gain water loss

b) Name the process by which water vapour diffuses out through the stomata of leaves. **1** — dKU **C**

____

[Model answers on page 93]

MARKS | STUDENT MARGIN

10 a) The graph shows how the intensity of grazing by rabbits affects the diversity of plant species in an area of grassland in Scotland.

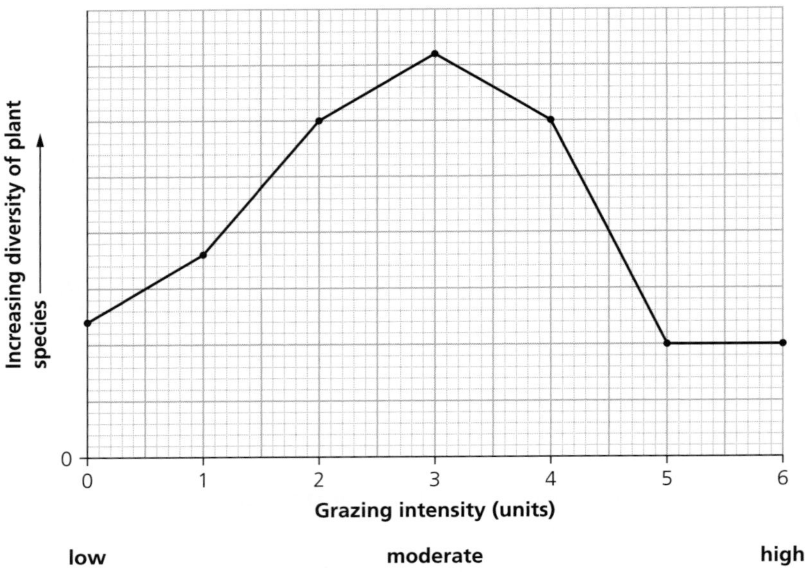

CAS KA3.1 Page 12

HTP Pages 97 and 147

b) Give **two** conclusions that can be made from the data shown in the graph. 2

1 ________________________________

2 ________________________________

Concluding

CA

c) Natural oak forests show a high species biodiversity.

Give the meaning of the term biodiversity. 1

dKU

C

d) Choose **one** of agriculture (other than grazing), house-building **or** industry and tick (✓) the appropriate box.

Agriculture (other than grazing) ☐ House-building ☐ Industry ☐

Explain how **your chosen** human activity could affect biodiversity. 2

Explanation ________________________________

CAS KA3.5 Page 13

HTP Page 119

aKU

CA

[Model answers on page 94]

	MARKS	STUDENT MARGIN
11 Invertebrate animals can be used to monitor pollution in streams and rivers. Students carried out a river study and used kick sampling as a method to collect invertebrates. They did this by marking out a 1 m^2 area of river-bed and positioned a 1 m-wide net downstream from the marked area. One student used their feet to gently move stones to dislodge the invertebrates. The invertebrates were caught in the net, identified and counted. This procedure was then repeated at different locations.		**CAS KA3.3,** P 13 **HTP,** P 109, 133, 135, 145, 146 and 147
a) State **two** variables that must be kept the same in this investigation. 1 ______ 2 ______	2	Planning **C**
b) Suggest one reason why the results from a sample might not be reliable. ______ ______	1	Evaluating **A**

c) The results of a study carried out to investigate the effect of sewage on populations of river invertebrates are shown in the graph below.

NUMBER OF INVERTEBRATES PER 3-MINUTE KICK SAMPLE

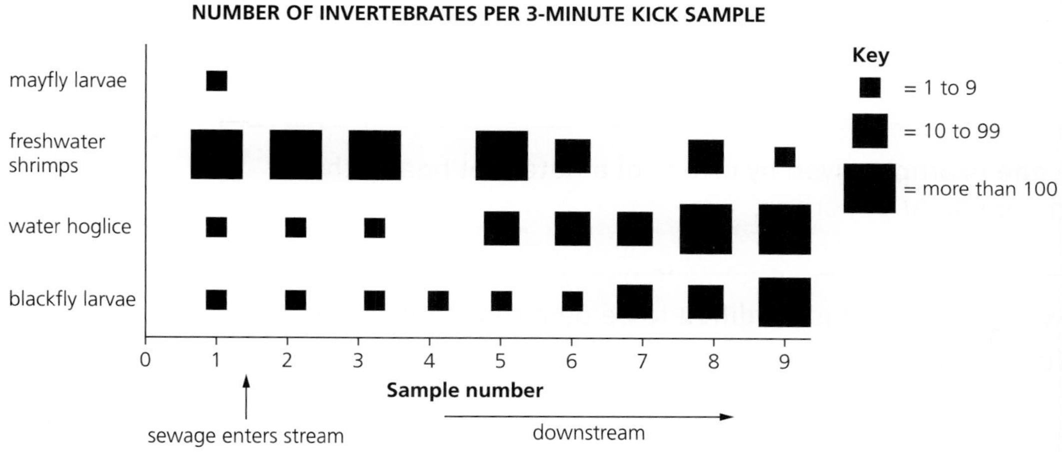

(i) Identify the range in number of water hoglice that could be found in sample 7. Tick (✓) the correct box. — 1 mark

1–9 ☐ 10–99 ☐ >100 ☐

(ii) Name the invertebrate that could best show that water is not polluted by sewage. — 1 mark

______

(Student margin: Selecting **C**)

d) Give the term used for organisms such as freshwater invertebrates that can be used to provide information about environmental factors. — 1 mark

______

(Student margin: dKU **C**)

[Model answers on pages 94–5]

MARKS | STUDENT MARGIN

12 a) Genetic modification of crops began with the discovery that the soil bacterium *Agrobacterium* could be used to transfer useful genes from unrelated species into plants. The Bt gene is one of the most commonly inserted. It produces a pesticide toxin that is harmless to humans but is capable of killing insect pests. Many new crop types have been produced and modified to be pest, disease or weedkiller resistant. They include wheat, potatoes, tomatoes and many others. Supporters argue that drought-resistant or salt-resistant varieties can grow well in poor conditions and that insect-repelling crops protect the environment by minimising pesticide use. Critics fear that genetically modified (GM) foods could have unforeseen effects. Toxic proteins might be produced or antibiotic-resistance genes may be transferred to human gut bacteria. Modified crops could also accidentally breed with wild plants or other crops. Investigations have shown that accidental gene transfer can occur.

CAS KA3.5 Page 13

HTP Pages 119, 133 and 146

Use information from the passage above to answer the following questions.

(i) Describe the role of the bacterium *Agrobacterium* in the genetic modification of crop plants. 1 — Selecting **C**

____

____

(ii) Give **one** example given by critics of a potential health threat from the use of GM crops. 1 — aKU **A**

____

b) Explain why a plant that is modified to be pest resistant could be

(i) useful to farmers 1 — aKU **A**

____

____

(ii) helpful to the environment. 1 — Selecting **C**

____

____

c) Methods of increasing food supply include biological control. State what is meant by the term biological control. 1 — dKU **A**

____

____

[Model answers on page 95]

[END OF PRACTICE PAPER B]

ADDITIONAL SPACE FOR ANSWERS AND ROUGH WORK

ADDITIONAL GRAPH PAPER FOR QUESTION 4a)

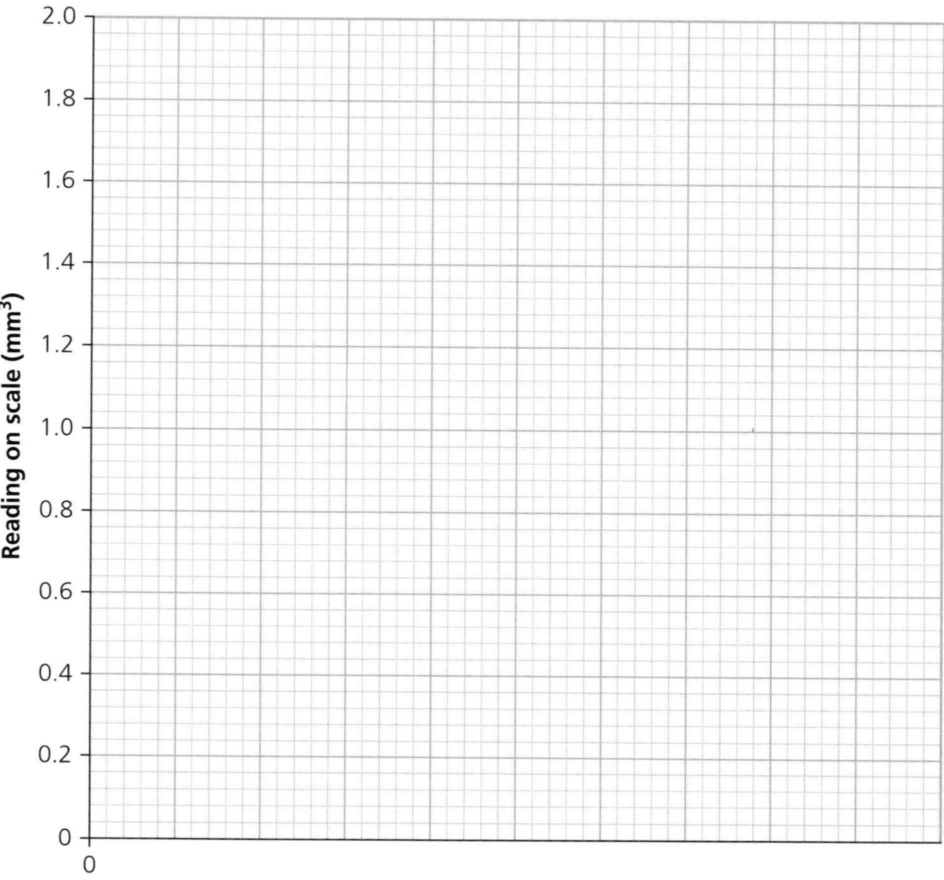

National 5 Biology

Section 1

SECTION 1 — 20 marks

Attempt ALL questions. Answer grid available at www.hoddereducation.co.uk/updatesandextras.

STUDENT MARGIN

1 Which line in the table below describes features of osmosis?

	Energy requirement	Substance moved	Direction of movement on concentration gradient
A	passive	water only	against
B	active	water-soluble substance	down
(C)	passive	water only	down
D	active	water-soluble substance	against

CAS KA1.2 Page 8
HTP Page 5
dKU
C

2 The diagram below shows the appearance of a plant cell after it had been left in a salt solution for one hour.

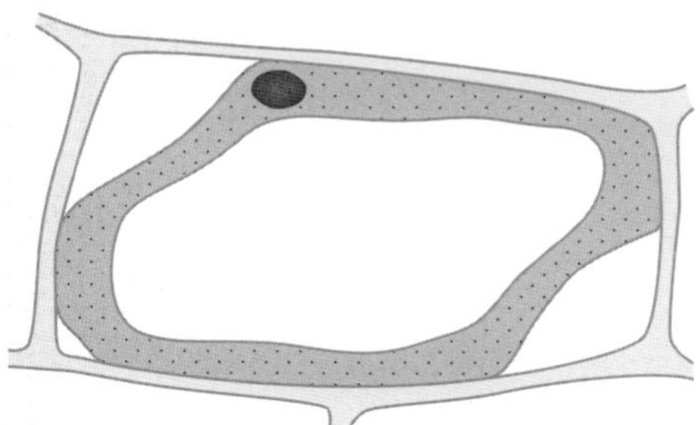

Which line in the table below indicates the strength of the salt solution and the term that describes the appearance of the cell?

	Strength of salt solution	Term
A	weak	plasmolysed
(B)	strong	plasmolysed
C	weak	turgid
D	strong	turgid

CAS KA1.2 Page 8
HTP Page 5
aKU
C

3 The list shows steps in the process of protein synthesis in cells.

1 mRNA leaves the nucleus
2 mRNA attaches to a ribosome
3 a complementary copy of the DNA code is produced
4 amino acids are assembled in sequence

In which order would these events occur?

A 1, 2, 4, 3
(B) 3, 1, 2, 4
C 4, 3, 1, 2
D 3, 4, 2, 1

STUDENT MARGIN

CAS KA1.4 Page 9
HTP Page 16
dKU
C

4 The diagram below represents stages involved in an enzyme controlled degradation reaction in a cell.

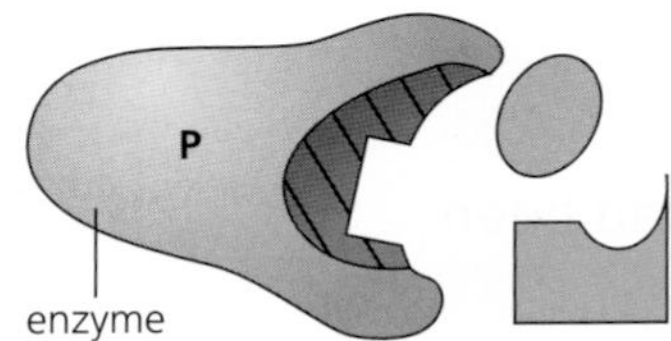

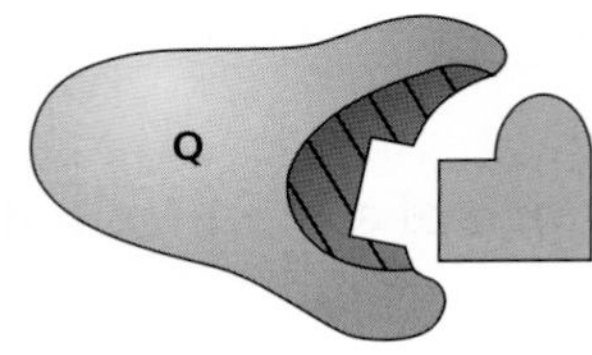

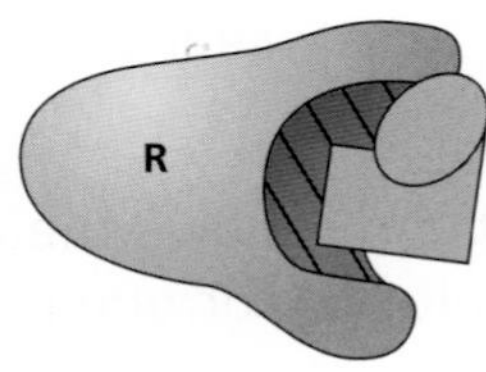

In which order would the stages be expected to occur?

A P, Q, R
B Q, P, R
C P, R, Q
(D) Q, R, P

CAS KA1.5 Page 9
HTP Page 19
aKU
C

5 The diagram below shows stages in the genetic engineering of a bacterial cell.

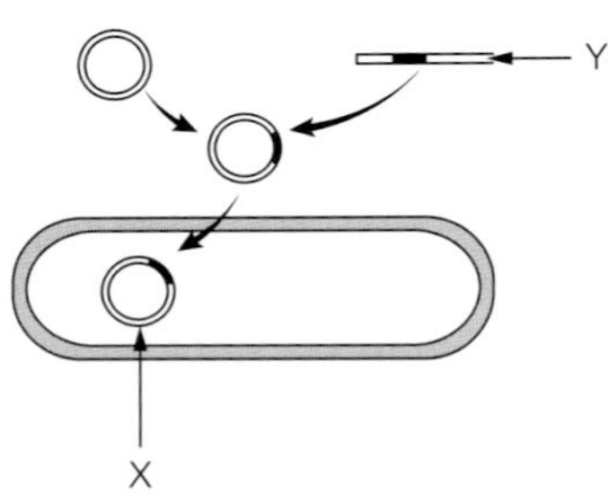

Which structures are represented by the letters X and Y?

	Structure X	Structure Y
(A)	plasmid	chromosome
B	nucleus	desired gene
~~(C)~~	plasmid	desired gene
D	nucleus	chromosome

CAS KA1.6 Page 9
HTP Page 23
aKU
C

6 The diagram below shows apparatus used to measure the rate of photosynthesis in a water plant. This is recorded as the number of bubbles of oxygen produced by the plant in one minute.

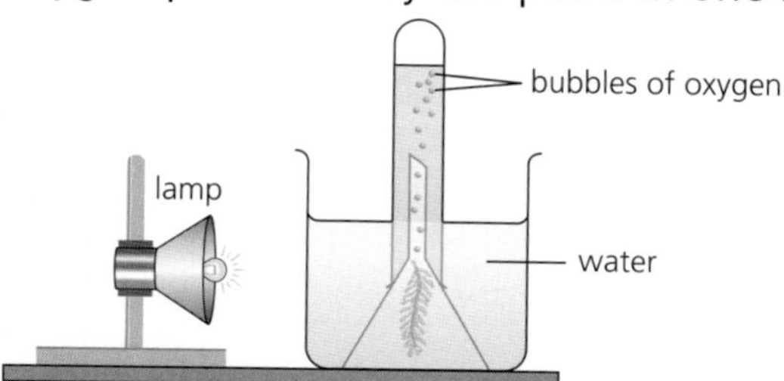

Which of the following changes to the apparatus would be expected to cause a decrease in the number of bubbles of oxygen produced per minute?

A move the lamp further away

B increase the temperature

C replace water with solution rich in carbon dioxide

D add more water plant sprigs

STUDENT MARGIN

CAS KA1.7 Page 9

HTP Pages 133 and 146

Predicting

C

7 One method of reproduction in potato plants involves the growth of shoots from potato tubers as shown in the visual below.

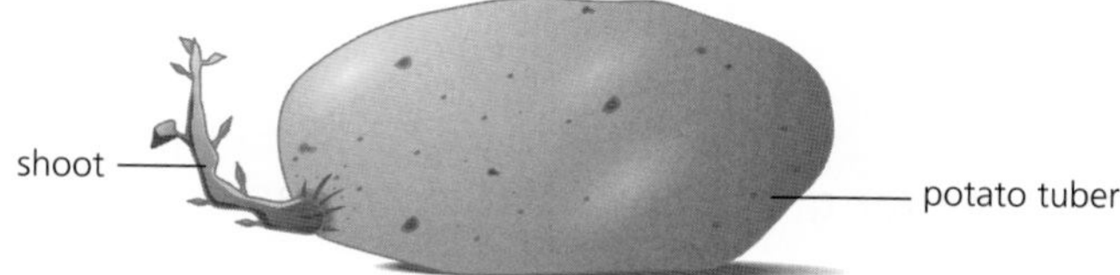

The graph below shows the average dry mass of samples of potato tubers and the shoots produced from them over an 8-week period.

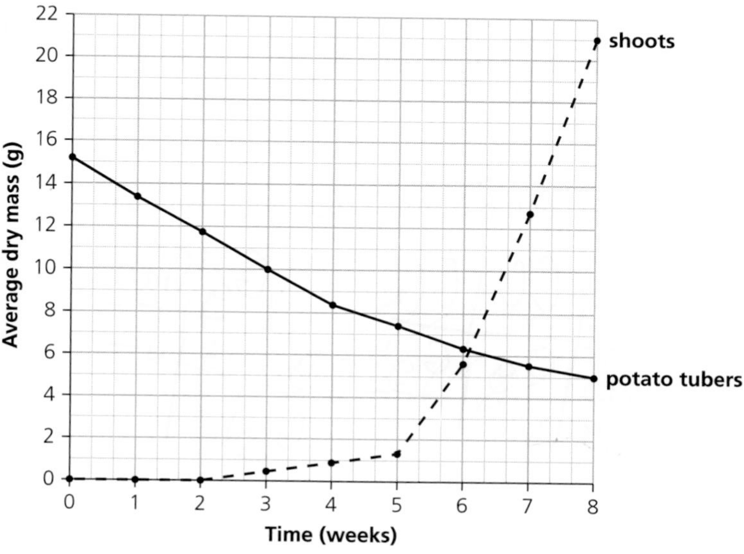

Which of the following statements is correct?

A The average dry mass of the shoots increased steadily.

B The weekly rate of increase in average dry mass of shoots was between weeks 5 and 6.

C The average dry mass of potato tubers and shoots was equal at week 6.

D The greatest difference in average dry mass of the potato tubers and shoots was at week 8.

CAS KA2.4 Page 11

HTP Pages 133 and 146

Selecting

A

8 The diagram below shows a summary of aerobic respiration in a cell.

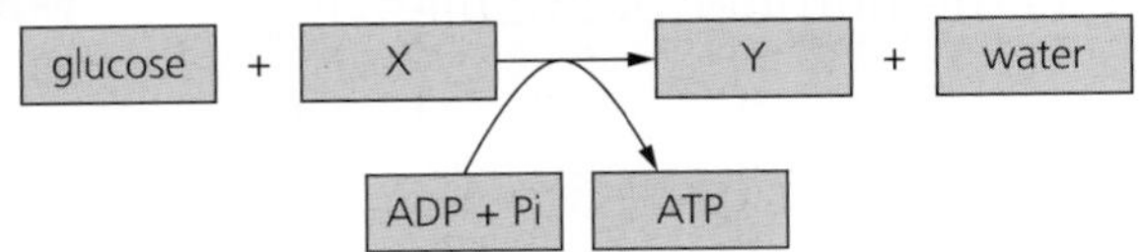

Which substances are represented by the letters X and Y?

	X	Y
A	carbon dioxide	oxygen
B	oxygen	lactic acid
C	oxygen	carbon dioxide
D	carbon dioxide	ethanol

9 Meristems are found at the shoots and root tips of flowering plants.

Which terms describe the cells present within meristems?

A haploid and specialised
B haploid and unspecialised
C diploid and specialised
D diploid and unspecialised

10 In the fruit fly *Drosophila melanogaster*, the allele for grey body (**G**) is dominant to the allele for black body (**g**).

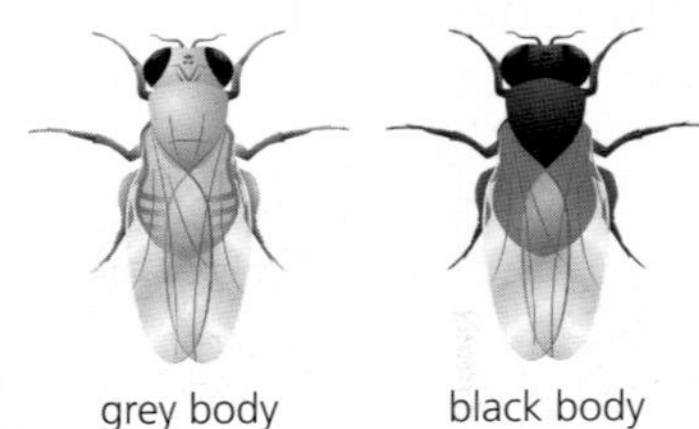
grey body black body

What ratio of offspring phenotypes would be expected from a cross between two heterozygous flies?

A 1 grey : 1 black
B 2 grey : 1 black
C 3 black : 1 grey
D 3 grey : 1 black

STUDENT MARGIN

CAS KA1.8 Page 10
HTP Page 32
dKU
C

CAS KA2.2 Page 10
HTP Page 51
dKU
C

CAS KA2.5 Page 11
HTP Page 66
aKU
A

11 As part of an investigation into variation, a sample of human volunteers had their hand spans measured. The results showed a wide range of values between a minimum and a maximum.

Which line in the table below describes characteristics such as hand span?

	Variation pattern	Inheritance pattern
(A)	continuous	polygenic
B	discrete	polygenic
C	continuous	single gene
D	discrete	single gene

12 The diagram below shows a section through a single villus from the human small intestine.

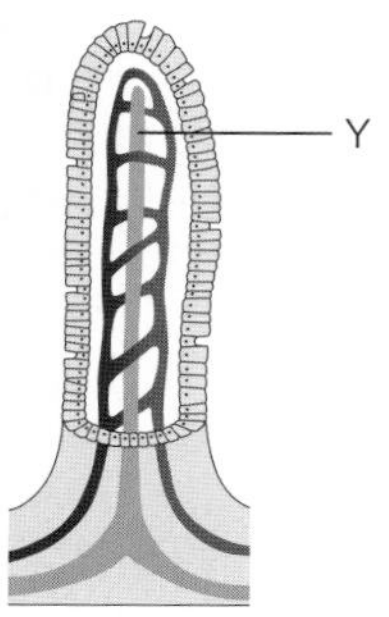

Which food molecules are absorbed by structure Y?

A amino acids
B fatty acids
C glucose
D glycogen

STUDENT MARGIN

CAS KA2.5 Page 11
HTP Page 66
aKU
C

CAS KA2.6 Page 11
HTP Page 71
dKU
C

13 The main breathing tubes in mammals have cartilage rings and are lined with cells that have cilia.

Which line in the table below shows the functions of cartilage rings and cilia?

	Cartilage rings	Cilia
A	hold airway open	trap microorganisms
B	carry out peristalsis	trap microorganisms
C	hold airway open	move mucus
D	carry out peristalsis	move mucus

STUDENT MARGIN

CAS KA2.6 Page 11

HTP Page 80

dKU

C

Questions 14 and 15 refer to the diagram, which shows the blood flow into and out of the human heart.

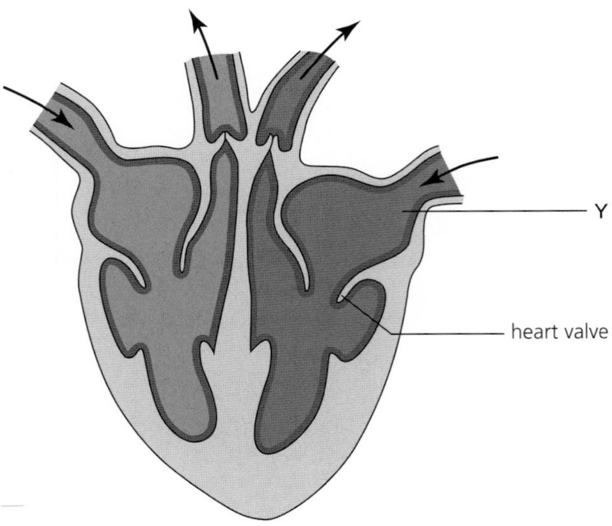

14 Blood vessel Y is the

A vena cava
B pulmonary vein
C pulmonary artery
D aorta

CAS KA2.6, P 11

HTP, P 74

dKU; C

15 What is the function of the heart valve shown?

A keeps blood flowing into the right ventricle
B stops blood flowing back into the right atrium
C keeps blood flowing into the left ventricle
D stops blood flowing back into the left atrium

CAS KA2.6, P 11

HTP, P 74

aKU; A

16 Which term refers to a region of the planet distinguished by its climate, flora and fauna?

A ecosystem
B habitat
C biome
D niche

CAS KA3.1, P 12

HTP, P 97

dKU; C

17 The diagram below shows the flow of energy through part of a woodland ecosystem.

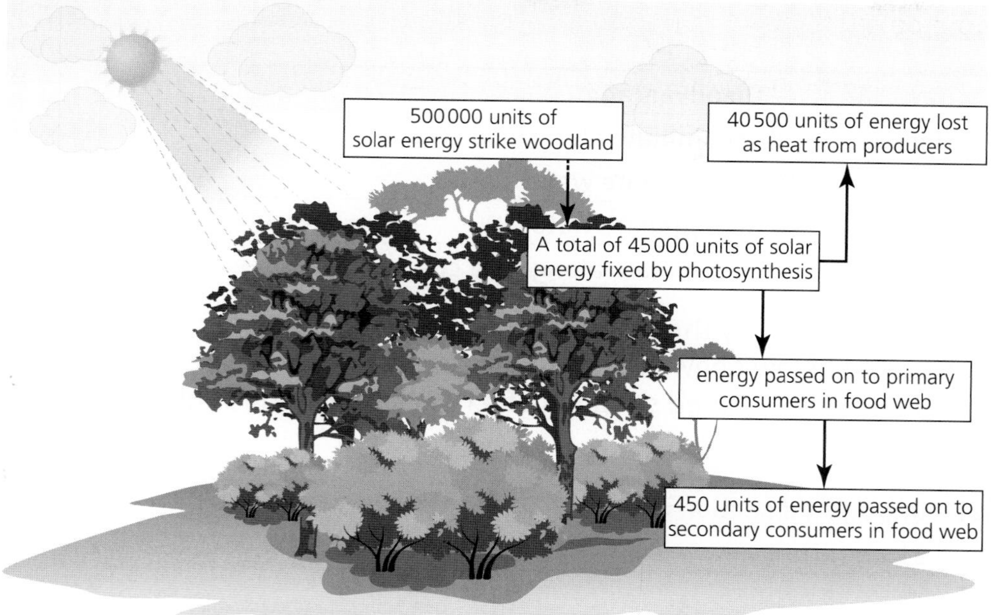

How many units of energy are available to be passed to primary consumers in the food web of this area of woodland?

A 415
B 450
C 4100
D 4500

18 A species of heather plant was surveyed on a Scottish hillside. 12 quadrats were placed randomly and the number of individual heather plants within each quadrat was counted. The results are shown in the diagram below.

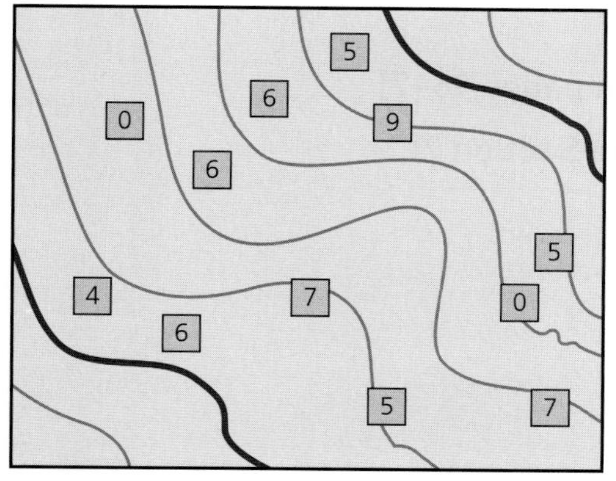

What was the average number of heather plants per quadrat on the area of hillside sampled?

A 5
B 6
C 30
D 60

STUDENT MARGIN

CAS KA3.2 Page 12
HTP Pages 134 and 146
Processing
A

CAS KA3.3 Page 13
HTP Pages 134 and 146
Processing
C

19 Pesticides have advantages and disadvantages for the human population.

Which line in the table below shows an advantage and a disadvantage of using pesticides?

	Advantage	Disadvantage
(A)	increase food yields	accumulate along food chains
B	improve biodiversity	deoxygenate water
C	increase food yields	deoxygenate water
D	improve biodiversity	accumulate along food chains

STUDENT MARGIN

CAS KA3.5 Page 13

HTP Page 119

aKU

A

20 Indicator species are species that, by their presence or absence, indicate levels of pollution. The table below shows the numbers of four invertebrate species found in unpolluted and polluted sections of a river that run through a polluted area.

Invertebrate species	Unpolluted section of river	Polluted section of river
mayfly larva	21	2
blackfly larva	35	29
hoglouse	13	12
midge larva	3	48

From the data shown, which species would appear to be the only indicators of pollution?

A mayfly larvae and hoglouse
(B) mayfly larvae and midge larvae
C blackfly larvae and midge larvae
D hoglice and blackfly larvae

CAS KA3.5 Page 13

HTP Pages 133 and 146

Selecting

C

[End of Section 1 — Answers on pages 96–7]

[Now attempt the questions in Section 2]

Section 2

SECTION 2 — 60 marks

Attempt ALL questions in this section.

Write your answers clearly in the spaces provided in this paper. Additional space for answers and rough work is provided at the end of this paper. If you use this space you must clearly identify the question number you are attempting. Any rough work must be written in this space. You should score through your rough work when you have written your final copy.

Use **blue** or **black** ink.

	MARKS	STUDENT MARGIN

1 The diagram below shows cells from the tip of a growing soil fungus.

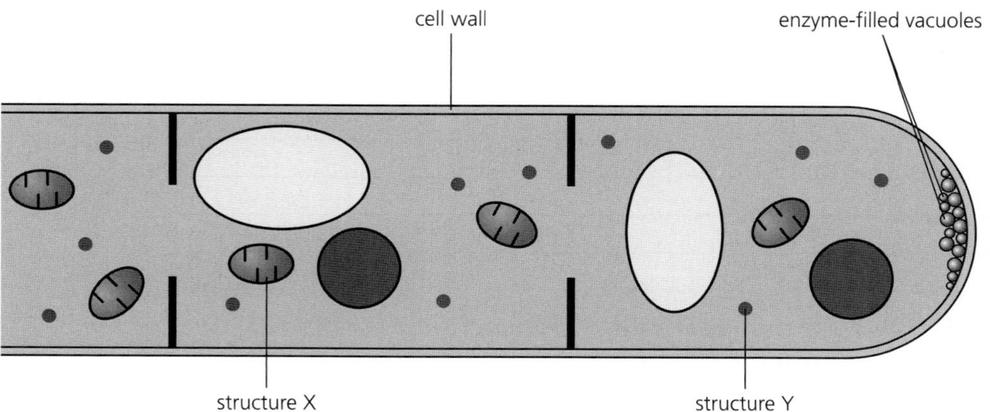

CAS KA1.1 Page 8

HTP Page 1

a) Complete the table below by entering the names of the structures shown. 2 — aKU CC

Structure	Name	Process associated with structure
X	mitochondria	aerobic respiration
Y	ribosome	protein synthesis

b) The fungal cells are different from green plant cells in several ways.

(i) State how their cell walls differ from those of a green plant cell. 1 — dKU C

They are not made from cellulose

(ii) Give **one** other difference between fungal and green plant cells. 1 — dKU C

Fungal cells don't have chloroplasts.

c) The fungus decomposes the tissues of dead organisms that have fallen into the soil.

Suggest the role played by the enzymes in the vacuoles during this process. 1 — aKU A

[Model answers on page 98]

C

MARKS | STUDENT MARGIN

2 An experiment was set up to investigate the effect of sucrose solutions on the mass of potato tissue. Strips of potato tissue were cut, weighed individually, and then placed into identical tubes containing sucrose solutions of different concentration as shown in the diagram below.

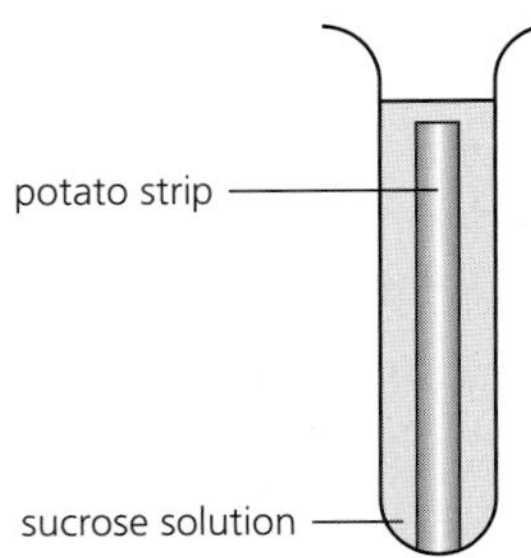

The strips were left in the solutions for one hour at 20 °C, then each was reweighed and their percentage changes in mass calculated. The results are shown in the table below.

Sucrose concentration (g/l)	Percentage change in mass of potato tissue
0	+20
20	+15
40	+5
60	−5
80	−10
100	−20

CAS KA1.2 Page 8

HTP Pages 5, 134, 135, 145 and 146

a) On the bar chart below:

(i) complete the scale and label on the vertical axis 1

(ii) draw in the missing bars to show how sucrose concentration affected the mass of potato tissue 1

(Additional graph paper, if required, can be found on page 77.)

Presenting

CC

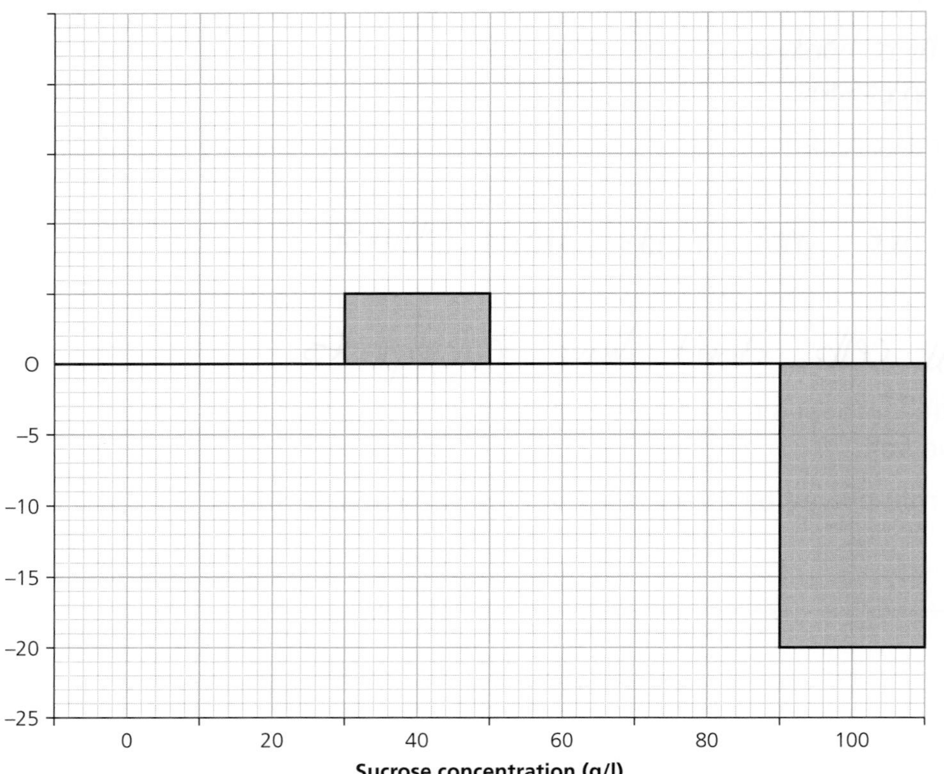

	MARKS	STUDENT MARGIN
b) **(i)** Name **one** variable, not already mentioned, which must be kept constant to allow valid conclusions to be made. ______________________________	1	Planning **C**
(ii) Suggest how the reliability of the results obtained could be increased. ______________________________	1	Planning **C**
c) Using the results given in the table, predict the sucrose concentration that would be expected to have no effect on the mass of potato tissue and justify your answer. Prediction ____________ g/l Justification ________________________ ______________________________ ______________________________ ______________________________	2	Predicting **CA**

[Model answers on page 98]

MARKS | STUDENT MARGIN

3 The diagram below shows a fermenter used for culturing cells on an industrial scale.

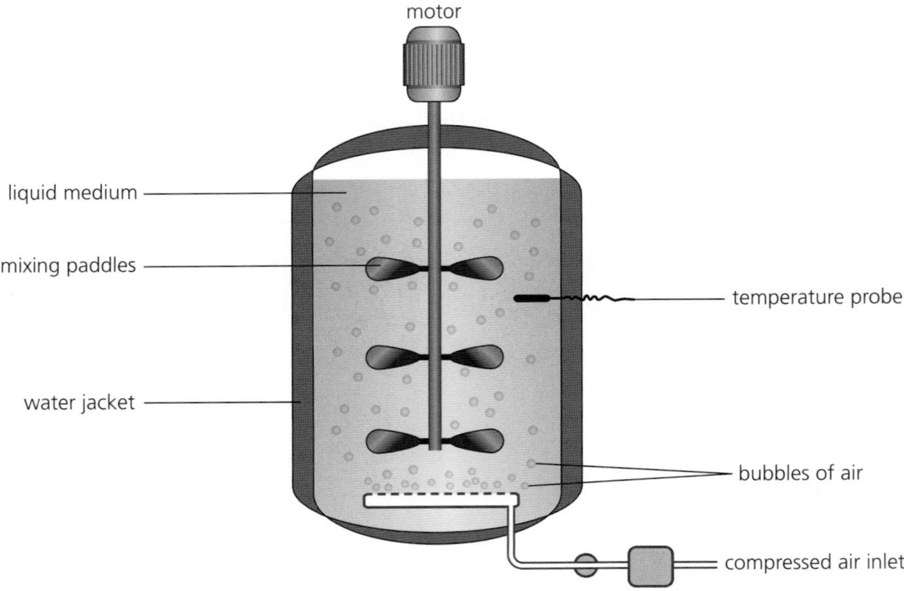

CAS KA1.3 Page 9

HTP Pages 12, 135 and 145

a) Explain why aseptic techniques are used when setting up and culturing cells in a fermenter such as this. 1 aKU C

____

____

b) Successful cell culture depends on the control of factors such as temperature and oxygen levels.

(i) Explain the importance of controlling temperature in a fermenter. 1 aKU C

____

____

(ii) **1** Describe how the supply of oxygen is ensured in the fermenter shown. 1 Planning C

____

2 Name the process carried out by growing cells which require oxygen 1 dKU C

____

____

c) The cells in the fermenter shown are supplied with an appropriate medium for their growth.

Name one substrate which could be needed by growing cells. 1 dKU C

____

[Model answers on page 99]

		MARKS	STUDENT MARGIN
4	DNA encodes the genetic information that is needed to make specific proteins in a cell. The diagram below represents part of a DNA molecule.		**CAS KA1.4** Page 9 **HTP** Page 16

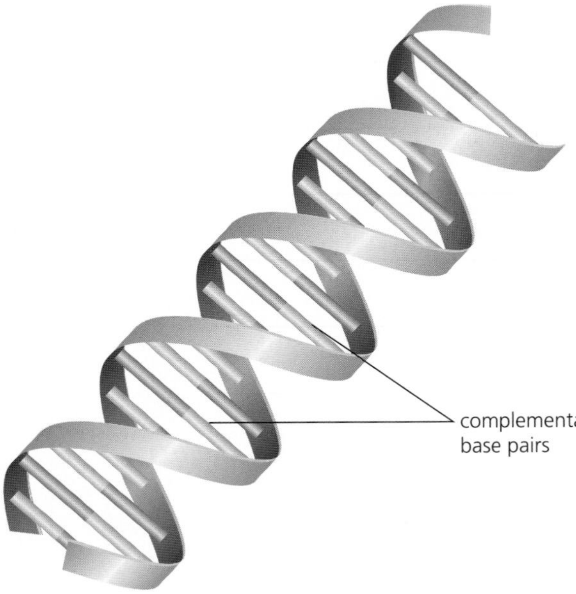

complementary base pairs

		MARKS	STUDENT MARGIN
a)	Using the names of the bases, explain what is meant by the term 'complementary' as shown in the diagram.	1	dKU **C**
b)	Describe how the DNA molecule determines the sequence of amino acids in a protein.	1	dKU **C**
c)	Describe the role of messenger RNA (mRNA) in the synthesis of proteins in cells.	2	dKU **CA**

[Model answers on page 99]

MARKS STUDENT MARGIN

5 Describe the main requirements and products of the light-dependent stage of photosynthesis. 4

CAS KA1.7 Page 9

HTP Page 27

dKU

CCCA

[Model answers on page 99]

6 The diagram below shows a group of human red blood cells.

MARKS	STUDENT MARGIN
	CAS KA2.1 Page 10 **HTP** Page 47

a) Give the term used for a group of similar cells, such as these, which work together to carry out a specific function. **1**

____

dKU **C**

b) Red blood cells are highly specialised for their function.

(i) Describe the function of red blood cells in the human body. **1**

____

(ii) Describe **one** adaptation of red blood cells and explain how it allows them to carry out their function efficiently. **2**

Description ______________________________

____

Explanation ______________________________

____

CAS KA2.6 Page 11 **HTP** Page 74 dKU **C**

dKU **CA**

[Model answers on pages 99–100]

	MARKS	STUDENT MARGIN

7 The diagram below shows some structures involved in a human reflex action.

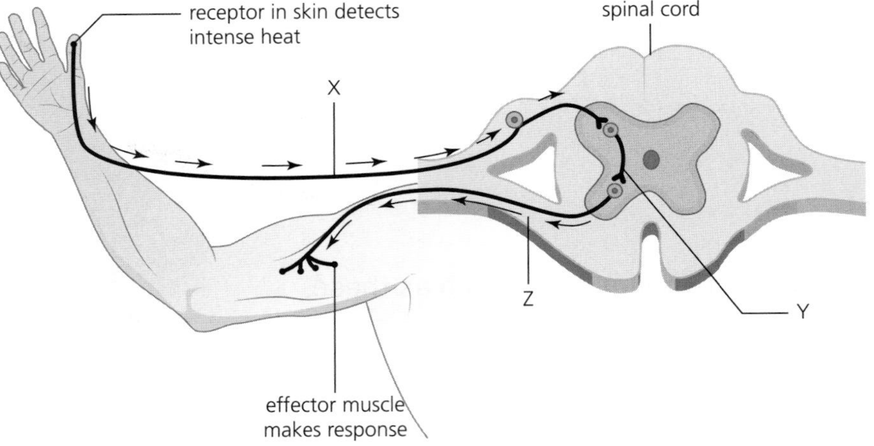

CAS KA2.3 Page 11

HTP Page 54

a) The cells labelled X, Y and Z are neurons involved in a reflex arc. Choose one of these neurons and tick (✓) the appropriate box.

X ☐ Y ☐ Z ☐

(i) Name this neuron. **1** dKU C

____

(ii) Describe the function of this neuron in the reflex arc. **1** dKU A

____

____

b) Neurons are separated by tiny gaps. Nervous messages can be transmitted across these gaps from one neuron to another.

(i) Name the gap between neurons. **1** dKU C

____

(ii) Describe how nervous messages can cross the gaps. **1** dKU A

____

____

____

c) Explain the advantage to a human of the reflex action shown in the diagram. **1** aKU A

____

____

[Model answers on page 100]

8 In an investigation into the effects of temperature on the rate of transpiration from leafy shoots, five sets of apparatus were set up as shown in the diagram. Each was left for the same length of time at a different temperature and the rate of transpiration from each was measured by reading the water level on the scale. It is assumed that all water taken up by the shoot was lost to the air.

MARKS	STUDENT MARGIN
	CAS KA2.6 Page 11 **HTP** Pages 71, 134, 135, 145, 146 and 147

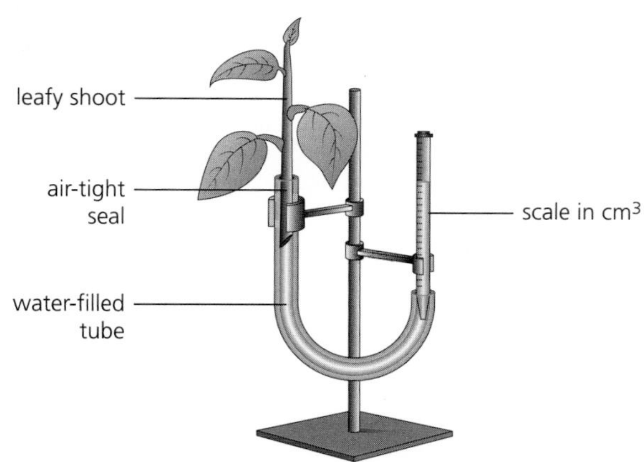

The results are shown in the table below.

Temperature (°C)	Average rate of transpiration (cm^3 per hour per cm^2 leaf surface)
5	0.2
10	0.3
15	0.5
20	0.7
25	1.2

a) Explain why the seal shown in the experimental apparatus above must be air-tight. 1 — Planning **A**

____

____

b) Explain why the transpiration rate was measured per cm^2 of leaf surface. 1 — Planning **A**

____

____

c) Explain why it is invalid to assume that all water taken up by a leafy shoot is lost in transpiration. 1 — Evaluating **A**

____

____

MARKS | STUDENT MARGIN

d) Calculate the percentage increase in the average rate of transpiration as the temperature was increased from 5 °C to 25 °C. 1

Space for calculation

Processing

A

_______________ %

[Model answers on page 100]

9 A study of breeding in sheep was carried out on a group of Scottish farms over a 10-year period. The histogram below shows how the birth mass of lambs born on the farms affected their survival over the first 10 days of life.

MARKS	STUDENT MARGIN
	CAS KA2.4 Page 11 HTP Pages 63, 133, 134, 146 and 147

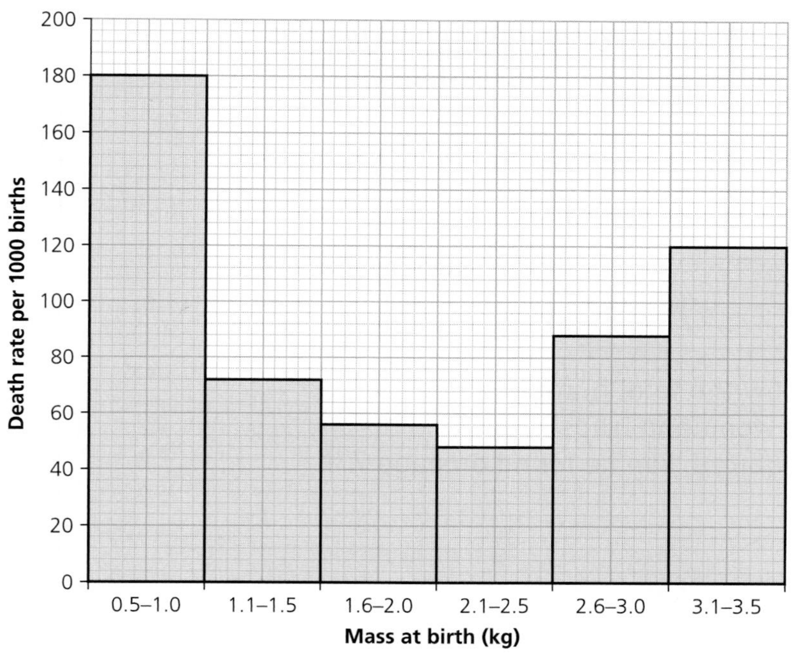

a) **(i)** Calculate the average death rate of all lambs in the study. *[1 mark — Processing A]*

Space for calculation

________________ deaths per 1000 births

(ii) State the range of the lambs' birth masses that would produce death rates less than 80 per 1000 births. *[1 mark — Selecting C]*

________________ kg to ________________ kg

(iii) Suggest one reason that would explain the higher death rates in the lambs with the lowest birth masses *[1 mark — Concluding A]*

____

(iv) What evidence is there that the heaviest lambs have problems during birth? *[1 mark — Concluding C]*

____

(b) Sheep are mammals.

Describe fertilisation in mammals. *[1 mark — dKU C]*

____

____

[Model answers on pages 100–1]

C

	MARKS	STUDENT MARGIN

10 In an investigation into the types and numbers of invertebrates in woodland compared with grassland, ten pitfall traps were set in each habitat. The invertebrates caught were identified and counted. The results are shown in the table.

CAS KA3.3 Page 13

HTP Pages 109, 134, 135, 145, 146 and 147

Invertebrate group	Total number of invertebrates found in traps	
	Woodland traps	Grassland traps
beetles	40	35
millipedes and centipedes	20	10
spiders and mites	10	15
springtails	0	30
slugs and snails	10	25

a) Complete the pie chart to show the total numbers of invertebrates found in the woodland traps. **2**
(An additional pie chart, if required, can be found on page 77)

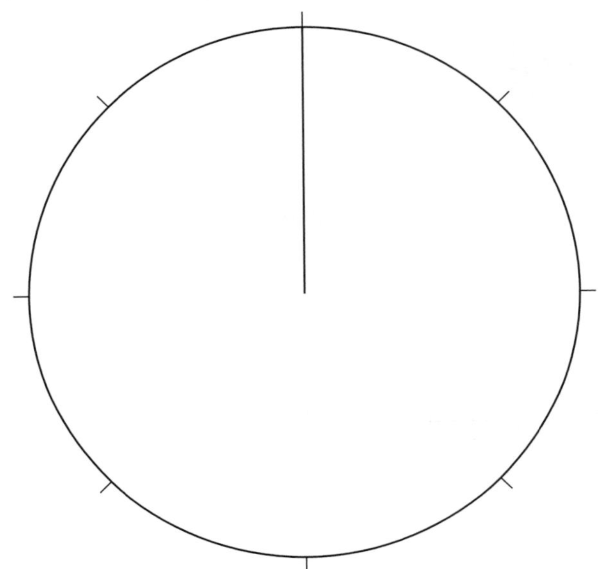

Presenting C

b) Calculate the simplest whole number ratio of snails and slugs in the woodland compared with the grassland. **1**

Space for calculation

_______________ : _______________

in woodland in grassland

Processing C

c) Explain why ten traps were set in each habitat. **1**

____

____

Planning C

	MARKS	STUDENT MARGIN
d) Explain why pitfall trapping does not sample all invertebrates living in a habitat.	1	Evaluating **A**
e) Suggest an abiotic factor that could account for the distribution of invertebrates in these habitats.	1	aKU **C**

[Model answers on page 101]

MARKS | STUDENT MARGIN

11 The flow chart below shows the events which followed the increased use of fertiliser in areas around the American Great Lakes in the 1960s.

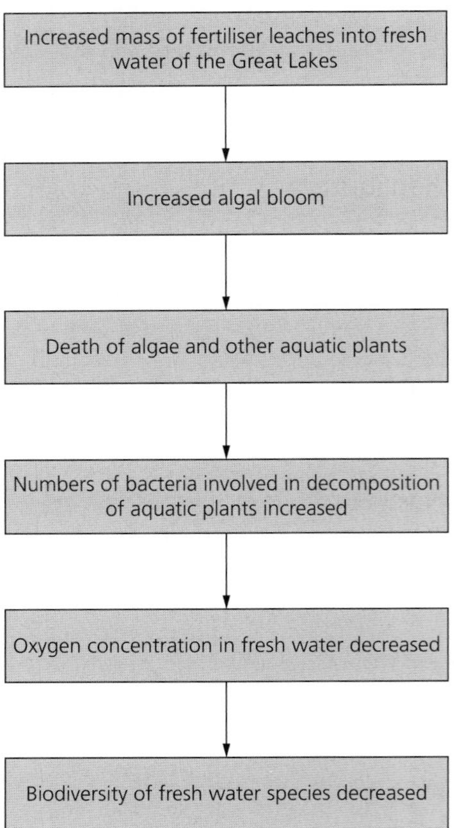

CAS KA3.5 Page 13

HTP Page 119,

a) Suggest a reason for the increase in fertiliser use in America in the 1960s. 1 — aKU **C**

____

b) Suggest what causes the death of the algae and other aquatic plants. 1 — aKU **C**

____

c) Select information that suggests that the bacteria responsible for the decomposition of aquatic plans are aerobic 1 — Selecting **C**

____

____

d) Use information from the flow chart to draw a conclusion about the effect of fertiliser use on biodiversity 1 — Concluding **C**

____

____

[Model answers on page 101]

	MARKS	STUDENT MARGIN
12 The diagram below shows part of the nitrogen cycle.		CAS KA3.2 Page 12 HTP Page 102

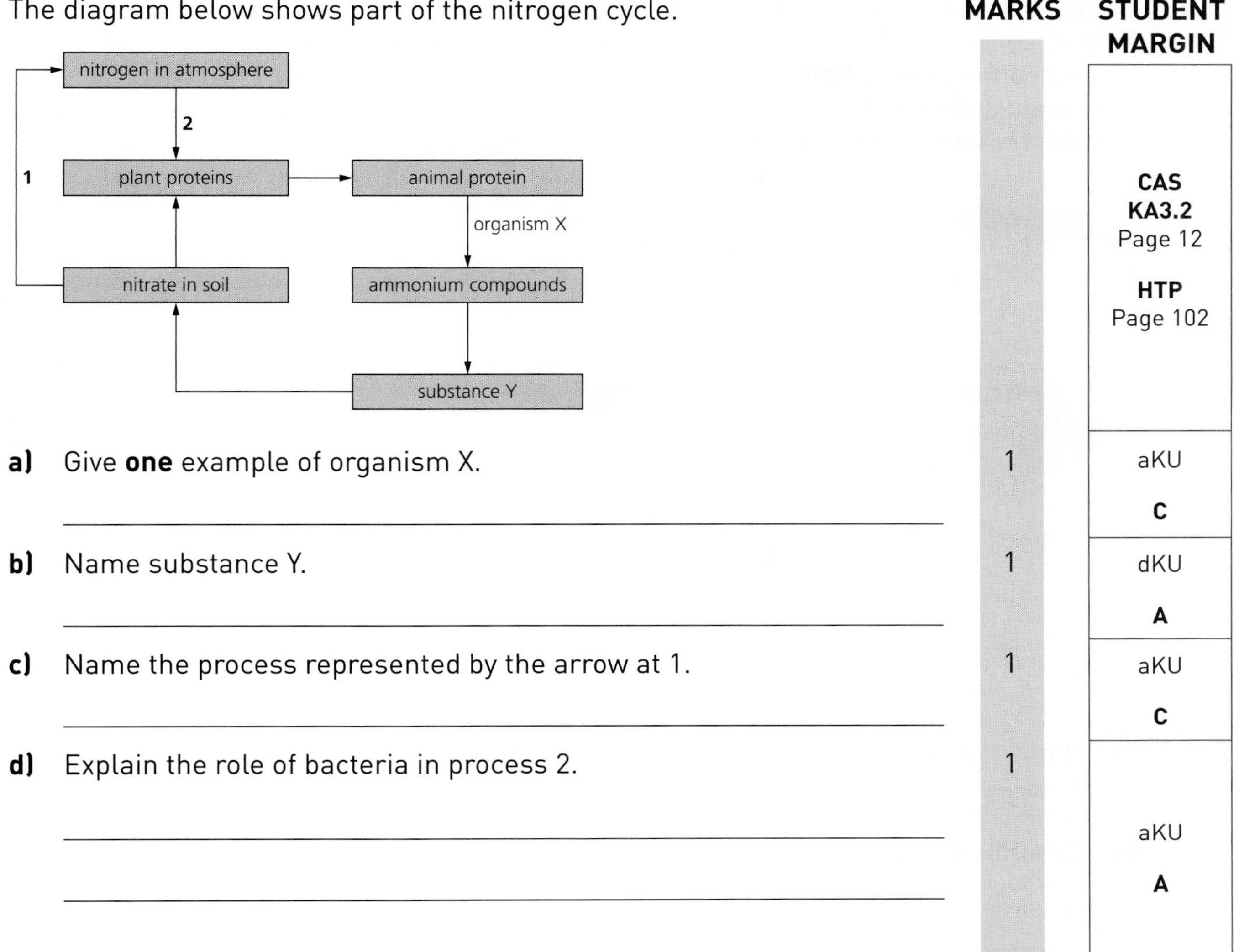

	MARKS	STUDENT MARGIN
a) Give **one** example of organism X.	1	aKU **C**
b) Name substance Y.	1	dKU **A**
c) Name the process represented by the arrow at 1.	1	aKU **C**
d) Explain the role of bacteria in process 2.	1	aKU **A**

[Model answers on page 101]

MARKS | STUDENT MARGIN

13 The diagram below shows the heads of four species of Hawaiian honeycreepers, the food items in which each specialises and the head of their common ancestor. The birds are all thought to have evolved after populations of their ancestor became isolated on the Hawaiian Islands, remote from the mainland, millions of years ago.

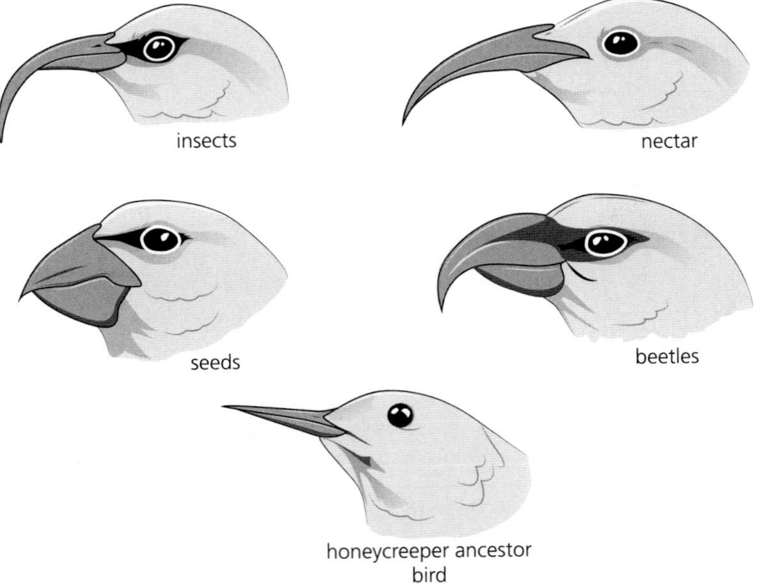

CAS KA3.4 Page 13

HTP Page 114

a) Name the type of isolation barrier involved in this example. 1 aKU **C**

____

b) Describe the roles played by mutation and natural selection in the evolution of the honeycreepers. 3 aKU **CAA**

____

____

____

____

____

____

____

____

[Model answers on page 102]

[END OF PRACTICE PAPER C]

ADDITIONAL SPACE FOR ANSWERS AND ROUGH WORK

ADDITIONAL GRAPH PAPER FOR QUESTION 2a)

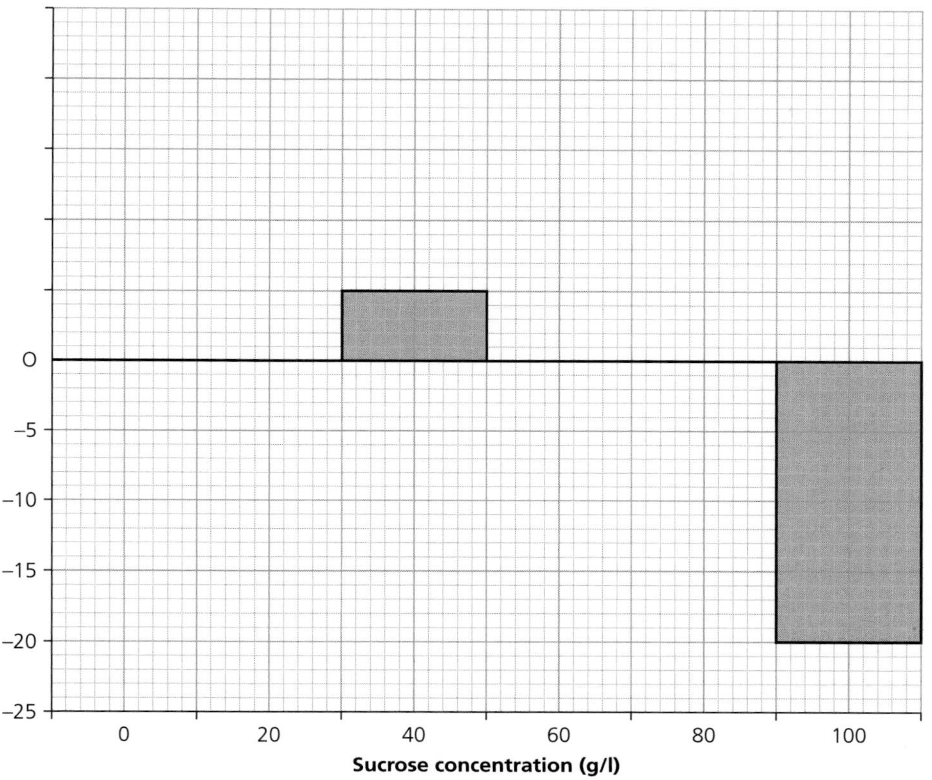

ADDITIONAL PIE CHART FOR QUESTION 10a)

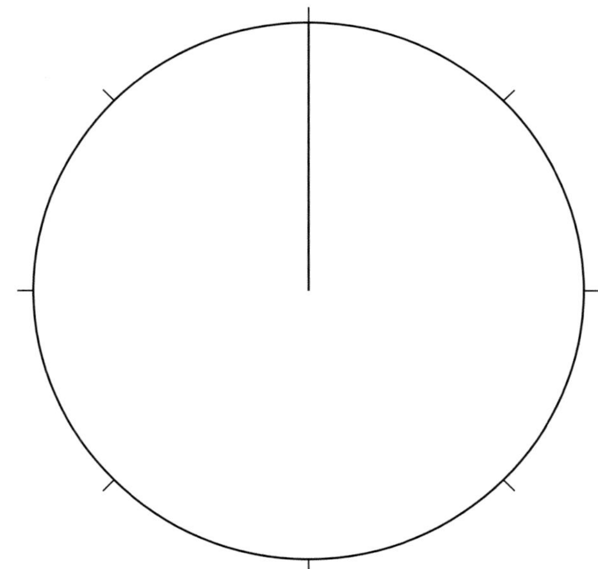

Answers

National 5 Biology

Practice Paper A

Section 1

Practice Paper A	Section 1 Objective Test		Commentary with hints and tips
Question	**Answer**	**Marks**	
1	**C**	1	mRNA is synthesised from DNA codes, which are in the nucleus – must be 1; sugars are made by photosynthesis, which occurs in chloroplasts – must be 4
2	**D**	1	Plant tissues that lose water by osmosis shrink and decrease in size (length in this case) – water has moved out of the potato in solution Y so answer D is the only description which would match this
3	**B**	1	Sequence of bases in DNA encodes the sequence of amino acids in protein
4	**A**	1	Selectively permeable membranes allow small molecules like glucose to pass through but restrict the movement of large molecules such as starch
5	**A**	1	Aerobic means requiring oxygen; lactic acid is a product of fermentation, which rules it out
6	**B**	1	Yeast can respire aerobically or by fermentation but ethanol is only produced in the fermentation pathway – the liquid paraffin layer keeps oxygen out and so conditions in tube B are correct for fermentation
7	**D**	1	Best tackled by thinking of the flow diagrams used to illustrate the sequence of events; it is essential to learn the vocabulary such as 'required gene' and 'source chromosome' here as well
8	**D**	1	Stem cells are not gametes so are diploid. They are non-specialised and retain the ability to divide by mitosis to produce more stem cells or to differentiate
9	**C**	1	There are many different flower shapes but female gametes are always produced in the ovary – C points to an ovule within an ovary
10	**B**	1	The key here is to note that the offspring grains are in a roughly 1:1 ratio of purple to yellow, then do the working for each of the options by working out gametes and possible offspring using Punnett squares
11	**D**	1	A good technique here is to add arrows to the diagram in the question to show where the blood in the main vessels is going; remember that the left side of the diagram is the right side of the person's heart

Practice Paper A	Section 1 Objective Test		Commentary with hints and tips
Question	**Answer**	**Marks**	
12	**B**	1	Proteins are activated by ATP to push substances against the concentration gradient – useful to imagine the concentration gradient as similar to the gradient of a hill, so energy is needed to move against the gradient
13	**A**	1	Tricky – the volume of drink given must be kept constant; the sugar concentration in drinks is the variable being altered and the volume of urine produced was being measured; the concentration of urine would vary but was not measured in the investigation
14	**A**	1	You must be able to link glycogen with the liver and glucagon with the pancreas and be able to locate these organs on the diagram
15	**B**	1	All about vocabulary – you need to remember the difference between biomes, ecosystems and niches
16	**A**	1	An algal bloom is a direct result of fertiliser release into streams and loch water; when the algae and larger aquatic plants eventually die, they are decomposed by aerobic bacteria, which use up oxygen
17	**C**	1	Species cannot interbreed with each other to form fertile offspring, so it follows that speciation cannot be complete until this point is reached
18	**C**	1	Bacteria are crucial in the nitrogen cycle; some species fix atmospheric nitrogen into nitrates – the species in this question live within the root nodules of plants such as peas, beans and clovers
19	**D**	1	Percentage changes are two-part calculations. First, calculate the change – in this case **60 – 30 = 30**; second, find this figure as a percentage of the starting value – in this case **30/30 × 100 = 100%**
20	**B**	1	Average calculations are two-part calculations. First add up all values – here these need to be read from the graph, ensuring that the N24 values are used: **280 + 300 + 380 = 960**; second, divide this total by the number of pieces of data involved – in this case **960/3 = 320**

Practice Paper A

Section 2

Practice Paper A			Section 2 Paper 2		Commentary with hints and tips
Question			Expected answer	Marks	
1	a)		Cell membrane	1	Label X points to the inside of the cell wall, which has the membrane pressed against it – notice the cell wall is already labelled
	b)		(Site of) protein synthesis/ assembly	1	Ribosomes are the sites to which mRNA carries a complementary copy of DNA codes from which proteins are assembled from amino acids
	c)		Plant cell wall made of cellulose **AND** bacterial cell wall made of different substances (than plant cell walls)/not made of cellulose	1	Cell wall structure in bacteria is different from in plant cells – it is **NOT** made from cellulose
	d)		In circular chromosome = 1 In plasmids = 1	2	DNA makes up genes, which are found in chromosomes such as the circular one shown; bacteria are unusual in that they have rings of DNA called plasmids, as shown but not labelled on the diagram
2	a)	(i)	Spindle forms = 1 Chromosomes/pair of chromatids line up on the equator = 1	2	Vocabulary once again crucial to allow the descriptions needed – spindle, chromosome, equator and, in part aii, the term chromatid – all visible in the diagrams
		(ii)	Chromatids separate/move apart	1	
	b)		Growth **AND** repair	1	Mitosis produces the new cells needed for growth and also for the repair of damaged tissue
3	a)	(i)	Reveal the position **AND** spacing of genes	1	In selecting the appropriate information, it is usually advisable to quote from the passage
		(ii)	Determine the order of the base pairs	1	
		(iii)	4%	1	The passage says that 100 000 genes were thought to be in each body cell and of those 4000 were thought to be responsible for genetic disease – **4000/100 000 × 100 = 4%**
		(iv)	Could jump-start/speed up medical research	1	Again, selecting and quoting is the best approach
		(v)	'... that were thought at that time ...' **OR** '... genes that were then suspected ...'	1	Here, you are obliged to quote

Practice Paper A			Section 2 Paper 2		Commentary with hints and tips
Question			Expected answer	Marks	
	b)		Adenine/A and thymine/T **OR** Guanine/G and cytosine/C	1	The base pairing rules need to be remembered – you can use letters if you want. **A**pples in **T**rees + **C**ars in **G**arages is a nice tip!
4	a)		Axes scale with zero **AND** labels with units = 1 Points plotted accurately **AND** connected with straight line = 1	2	With line graphs it is essential to ensure that the origin has scale numbers – not always zeros! Always use the table headings and units to label the axes Plot each point accurately (dots probably advisable) and connect the plots with straight lines – ruler essential
	b)		46.5 mg	1	At 25 °C the value would be halfway between 12 and 19, i.e. **15.5 for one hour**; for three hours **15.5 × 3 = 46.5 mg**
	c)	(i)	Repeat experiment at each temperature (and calculate average results)	1	Reliability is strengthened by repeating and very often the repeats would be averaged, so remember **ROAR** – **R**epeat and **O**btain an **A**verage to increase **R**eliability; it is important to say that repeats were done at each temperature
		(ii)	Temperatures just above or below 40 °C were not tested	1	The experimenters did not test 39 °C or 41 °C, so it is not possible to be definite about 40 °C being the optimum
	d)		Lipase – fats Catalase – hydrogen peroxide Pepsin – proteins **Others, but must match**	1	You must be able to give your own examples of enzymes with their specific substrate (and product(s))
5	a)	(i)	At upper surface of leaf **AND** in light Densely packed to increase number of cells Many chloroplasts **Any 1**	1	You can select any adaptation you like but it has to relate to photosynthesis and therefore is likely to be connected to light or chloroplasts
		(ii)	From xylem in vein to (spongy) mesophyll cell From mesophyll cell to air space From air space (through gap between guard cells) to atmosphere **All three arrows OR one continuous arrow through structures mentioned**	1	Water moves from xylem into the spongy mesophyll by **osmosis** but then **evaporates** into air spaces before **diffusing** out through the stomata
		(iii)	Lignin	1	Xylem vessels are dead and contain lignin for support

Practice Paper A			Section 2 Paper 2		Commentary with hints and tips
Question			Expected answer	Marks	
	b)		More stomata in lower epidermis than upper epidermis No stomata in upper epidermis of trees Tree leaves have higher numbers of stomata than other plants **Any two, 1 mark each**	2	You need to give a generalisation that can be seen from the numbers – there are several possibilities
6	a)	(i)	3 : 4	1	Be careful to select the correct figures from the graph as 60 : 80 – then find the lowest common factor of 20 to give a whole number ratio of 3 : 4
		(ii)	S – light intensity = 1 T – temperature = 1	2	The *x*-axis variable is limiting where the graph line above the axis is sloping but when the graph line is horizontal, another factor is limiting and you will need to look for information from the graph to identify it
	b)	(i)	Sugar/glucose/carbohydrate/starch	1	Photosynthesis produces oxygen as a final product of the light reactions and sugar as a product of carbon fixation – the sugar is glucose, which can be converted to the storage carbohydrate starch
		(ii)	Water/H_2O	1	Water is H_2O, the source of the oxygen (O_2)
7	a)	(i)	Tissue	1	Cells make up tissues and tissues are grouped into organs
		(ii)	Root = 1 Increased/large surface area for absorption = 1	2	Root hair cells are elongated into finger-like processes which increase the surface area through which absorption can occur
	b)		Group of organs working together	1	Organs are grouped into systems (and systems make up whole organisms)
8	a)		Names – W: cerebrum, Y: medulla = 1 Function – balance/co-ordination = 1	2	No real problems here but don't confuse cerebrum with cerebellum
	b)		Only target tissues have (cells with) the correct/matching/complementary/specific receptor protein in their membranes	1	Knowledge of how the specific receptor proteins are shaped to match the appropriate hormone needed
9	a)		A and B are tasters but have a child who is a non-taster	1	Both A and B must have the non-taster allele to pass to D but they don't show its effect, so it is recessive
	b)		Taster male	1	Remember that gender is part of the phenotype here
	c)		0%	1	Both parents are homozygous recessive so it is impossible for them to have a taster child

Practice Paper A			Section 2 Paper 2		Commentary with hints and tips
Question			**Expected answer**	**Marks**	
	d)		Discrete	1	Discrete variables fall into groups and do not show a range of variation
10	a)	(i)	As altitude increases, red blood cell count increases **OR** As altitude decreases, red blood cell count decreases **OR** Red blood cell count varies with/is proportional to altitude	1	In this question you need to look at both graphs and see how one affects the other. There are various ways that this relationship can be expressed
		(ii)	Day 34	1	This is where a coloured highlighter would be useful – just draw a line across from 6 million on Graph 2 and then a vertical line down to the *x*-axis and read the day number
		(iii)	1.1 million cells	1	Select lowest and highest values from Graph 2 then subtract to obtain the range
	b)	(i)	More efficient absorption of oxygen is needed because oxygen levels are lower at higher altitudes	1	This requires a bit of information from the stem of the question, which confirms that oxygen levels in the atmosphere are lower at higher altitude; since red cells absorb oxygen, having more of them will increase the efficiency of absorption at the higher altitude
		(ii)	Haemoglobin	1	Just have to know the term!
11			1 Competition involves a struggle for survival/scarce resources 2 Interspecific competition 3 occurs between members of different species (for similar resources) 4 Intraspecific competition 5 occurs between members of the same species (for same resources) **Any four, 1 mark each**	4	For extended responses, you have to focus in on a group of related facts. Take your time on these questions – at least 6 minutes; you might want to note down the key terms as a mini-plan before writing your answer
12	a)		1 Sprayed onto crops/fields 2 Washed off/leached into water/river/loch 3 Absorbed by water plants **Point 2 = 1 mark, point 1 or 3 = 1 mark**	2	You have to know that pesticides are sprayed onto crops and then you need to infer that, like fertilisers, they leach into water in rivers and lochs and they must be absorbed by water plants because they appear in the food chain
	b)		Passed on with every food item eaten = 1 Not broken down/accumulates/magnifies = 1	2	Remember that pesticide can be passed along food chains in the food items. It accumulates because there are no enzymes to break it down and it is not excreted

Practice Paper A			Section 2 Paper 2		Commentary with hints and tips
Question			**Expected answer**	**Marks**	
	c)		Use of a natural disease/ parasite/predator to control a pest	1	You need to recognise the term **bio**logical control – since **bio** means 'life', this means control through use of another living organism
13	**a)**		*Picea sitchensis* Needle tips notched *Abies procera* **All 3 = 2; any 1/2 = 1**	2	This is about taking information from the data table and knowing how it should be converted into the paired statement key. Use the headings and terms given in the table
	b)	**(i)**	Quadrat – dropped randomly **AND** contents counted/identified **OR** Pitfall trap – dug into ground **AND** left overnight (before being emptied) **OR** contents counted/ identified	1	It's your choice but make sure you are able to answer **both** parts of the question
		(ii)	Quadrat – not enough quadrats used **OR** quadrats not dropped randomly **OR** Pitfall trap – not enough traps laid **OR** traps not located randomly **OR** traps left too long before being checked **OR** traps not level with soil surface	1	Errors are often to do with loss of reliability, which comes with not taking enough samples or the validity problems of not making them random
[END OF PRACTICE PAPER A ANSWERS]					

Practice Paper B

Section 1

Practice Paper B	Section 1 Objective Test		Commentary with hints and tips
Question	**Answer**	**Marks**	
1	C	1	You need to know that plant, fungal and bacterial cell walls differ in structure and composition, and specifically that plant cell walls are made of cellulose
2	A	1	Remember – bacterial cells do not contain any organelles
3	B	1	Mitosis results in two diploid and genetically identical daughter cells
4	B	1	Add up the values provided and then divide the total by the number of values given – **876/4 = 219**
5	D	1	**SHARE** this tip – **S**tructural, **H**ormones, **A**ntibodies, **R**eceptors and **E**nzymes are proteins, which are composed of amino acids
6	A	1	The light energy produces ATP from ADP + Pi and splits water to provide the hydrogen needed in the carbon fixation stage
7	C	1	Any mention of lactic acid or ethanol indicates fermentation respiration and so 'C' is the only option.
8	D	1	When the graph slopes, the limiting factor is on the *x*-axis. If the graph line is flat, another factor is limiting – notice the effect of increased temperature
9	C	1	Water enters root hair cells by osmosis
10	B	1	A tissue is made from a group of specialised cells with similar structures and functions. An organ is made up of a group of different tissues working together to perform a particular function
11	A	1	Remember: **SS** = Sense organ → Sensory neuron **MM** = Motor neuron → Muscle (effector)
12	C	1	Medulla **below** the other brain structures controls functions such as breathing, heart rate and peristalsis, which are **below** the conscious level of thought
13	D	1	Remember – continuous variation shows a range of values that merge into each other – the values are not clear-cut
14	A	1	This condition only occurs when an individual inherits a recessive allele from both parents. Since neither parents were affected by the condition, they must have been heterozygous (carriers) for the condition

Practice Paper B	Section 1 Objective Test		Commentary with hints and tips
Question	Answer	Marks	
15	B	1	12.5% of 120 is **(120/100) × 12.5 = 15**
16	D	1	Four bowls (4 × 30 g = 120 g) are needed to provide 6 mg. However, since only 25% is absorbed we need to multiply this by four: **4 × 120 = 480**
17	D	1	In a laboratory situation, interspecific competition should cause one species to increase its population at the expense of its competitor
18	B	1	Remember – if it looks like a tree, it probably starts with a tree
19	C	1	You should have spotted the reference to competition, which is a biotic factor, and that quadrats are used for plants or non-moving animals mainly and therefore not suitable for investigations on invertebrates in leaf litter
20	A	1	Remember **ROLF** = mutations are of **R**andom **O**ccurrence and **L**ow **F**requency

Practice Paper B

Section 2

Practice Paper B			Section 2 Paper 2		Commentary with hints and tips
Question			**Expected answer**	**Marks**	
1	a)		S – protein = 1 T – phospholipid = 1	2	The **p**atchy molecules in the membrane are the **p**roteins. Remember – **PP** = **P**atchy **P**roteins
	b)	(i)	The movement of substances from a higher concentration to a lower concentration/down a concentration gradient	1	Key terms in diffusion answers are **DD** = **D**iffusion **D**own concentration gradient and **DD** = **D**issolve to **D**iffuse
		(ii)	Provide a large/increased surface area	1	Many topics in biology refer to the advantage of structures providing a large surface area, e.g. villi, microvilli, red blood cells, alveoli and root hair cells
	c)		Provides the cell with raw materials for respiration **OR** helps to remove waste products **OR** example – glucose and oxygen for respiration to provide energy	1	Remember **GORE!** **G**lucose and **O**xygen for **R**espiration and **E**nergy
2	a)		False, proteins = 1 True = 1 True = 1	3	DNA bases are A–T and G–C
	b)		600	1	If 20% are A then 20% must be T. This leaves 60%, of which **30% must be G** and 30% C. Then change 30% to a decimal and multiply by the total number: **0.30 × 2000 = 600**
	c)		Ribosomes	1	You must be able to identify cell structures from diagrams and know their functions
3	a)		Fertilisation in animals/plants **OR** transfer of plasmids between bacteria **OR** by viruses	1	Remember that transfer of genetic material happens naturally as well as artificially – make sure you know examples of each

Practice Paper B			Section 2 Paper 2		Commentary with hints and tips
Question			Expected answer	Marks	
	b)		1 Required gene identified/ located 2 Gene removed from chromosome (enzymes used) 3 Plasmid removed from bacterial cell 4 Gene inserted into plasmid/ vector 5 (Modified) plasmid inserted into (new) bacterial/host cell 6 Bacterial cells grown/cultured/ multiply 7 Insulin/required product extracted/purified/made **Items 2 and 4 plus any other 2, 1 mark each**	4	For extended responses, you have to focus in on a group of related facts. Take your time on these questions – at least 6 minutes; you might want to note down the key terms as a mini-plan before writing your answer Copy these steps out on paper and then cut into strips and practise putting them into the correct sequence!
4	a)		Axes, scale **AND** label = 1 Plotting points correctly **AND** connecting with straight lines = 1	2	Include zeros and highest values on even scales. Include units with label. Plot with a sharp pencil. Connect plots with straight lines
	b)	(i)	Repeat/set up the experiment/ apparatus in exactly the same way but do not include the snail	1	Control experiments are set up to make a comparison. The control should be identical to the original experiment apart from the one factor being investigated. Make sure you describe it in full
		(ii)	To absorb any carbon dioxide produced by the snail so that any change is due to oxygen	1	You need to know how a respirometer works and this is a crucial point
	c)		0.2 mm^3 oxygen per minute	1	First you need to notice that the rate of oxygen uptake is asked for **per minute**. This means that you need to calculate how much has been taken up in 10 minutes and then divide by 10: **2.0/10 = 0.2**
	d)		4.0 mm^3	1	Since there are two snails, you would need to double the 10 minute value: **2 × 2.0 = 4.0**
5	a)		Two matching sets = 1 Diploid = 1	2	These cells have been produced following mitosis so they must be genetically identical and diploid
	b)		Unspecialised/undifferentiated	1	Because they are undifferentiated they retain the potential to become almost any type of cell
	c)		Biconcave shape no nucleus contains haemoglobin **Any two, 1 mark each**	2	Biconcave shape increases the surface area for absorption and no nucleus leaves extra space for haemoglobin. Haemoglobin transports oxygen effectively in the form of oxyhaemoglobin.

Practice Paper B			Section 2 Paper 2		Commentary with hints and tips
Question			**Expected answer**	**Marks**	
6	**a)**	**(i)**	Glycogen	1	Take care with spelling here – often mixed up with glucagon
		(ii)	X – insulin = 1 Y – glucagon = 1	2	A useful rhyme ... Low blood sugar – glucose gone, what you need is glucagon. To turn glucose into glycogen, what you need is insulin. GLUCAGON is needed when GLUCOSE is GONE
	b)	**(i)**	36 per 1000 of population	1	First, work out the value of the scale – each small division has a value of 4. The number of females aged 65–74 = 112. Next, subtract the number of females below 65. Be careful to include **both** 45–64 **and** 0–44. So, **112 – 76 = 36**
		(ii)	Between 0–44 and 45–64	1	Count the boxes between each age range
7			Flowering plants: 1 (Male) pollen made in anthers 2 (Female) ovules made in ovaries 3 Pollen/ovules/gametes are haploid 4 Pollen nucleus fuses with ovule nucleus 5 To produce Zygote. **Point 4, 1 mark plus any other 2, 1 mark each** **OR** Animals: 1 (Male) sperm produced in the testes 2 (Female) ova made in ovaries 3 Sperm/ova/gametes are haploid 4 Sperm nucleus fuses with ovum nucleus 5 To produce a zygote **Point 4, 1 mark plus any other 2, 1 mark each**	3	In choice questions such as this it is worth spending a minute writing down key terms or phrases that come to mind to determine which one will give you the most marks For extended responses, you have to focus in on a group of related facts. Take your time on these questions – at least 5 minutes for this one

Practice Paper B			Section 2 Paper 2		Commentary with hints and tips
Question			**Expected answer**	**Marks**	
8	**a)**	**(i)**	NN X nn	1	Remember – two letters for each genotype. Homo = the same letters; hetero = different letters
		(ii)	Nn	1	Remember the rule: homozygous X homozygous = heterozygous
		(iii)	Normal wings	1	Remember – the phenotype is the observable characteristics of an organism as a result of its genes
		(iv)	75%	1	Remember the rule: heterozygous X heterozygous = 3:1 phenotype ratio
	b)		Inheritance determined by the interaction of several/many genes acting together	1	Another key term and definition that must be learned. Remember – poly = many
9	**a)**	**(i)**	1 Between 3 am and 6 am the rate of water loss remains constant at 4 g/min 2 It then increases to 50 g/min at 3 pm 3 It then decreases/returns to 4 g/min by 12 midnight/am 4 It remains constant/at 4 g/min (till 3 am) **All four with values and units = 2 marks** **Two or three correct = 1 mark** **All times and trends correct with no units = 1 mark**	2	When you are asked to describe a trend it is essential that you quote the values of the appropriate points and use the exact labels given on the axes in your answer. You must use the correct units in your description
		(ii)	400%	1	First, calculate the change – increase. Next, express this value as a percentage: $\frac{\textbf{increase}}{\textbf{starting value}} \times 100$, i.e. $\frac{32}{8} \times 100 = 400$
		(iii)	2:1	1	Take care that you present the ratio values in the order they are stated in the question. Simplify them by dividing the larger number by the smaller one, then dividing the smaller one by itself. However, if this does not give a whole number then you need to find another number that will divide into both of them
	b)		Transpiration	1	Another key term that you could add to your flash cards

Practice Paper B			Section 2 Paper 2		Commentary with hints and tips
Question			**Expected answer**	**Marks**	
10	a)		1 Moderate grazing (or named values: 2, 3) increases/gives higher species diversity **OR** As grazing intensity increases from low/1 to moderate/3, the species diversity increases 2 Low/0 intensity decreases/gives low species diversity 3 High grazing/5/6 decreases/gives low species diversity **OR** As grazing intensity increases from moderate/3 to high/6, the species diversity decreases **Any two, 1 mark each**	2	Study the graph carefully, noting the labels and data. Look for trends or specific features that could be compared or commented upon
	b)		The number/abundance/variety of species	1	Diversity = variety; bio = life Another definition that should be known
	c)		Agriculture – Named example of chemical or practice and the impact on biodiversity, e.g. removal of woodlands for agriculture/fertiliser leakage/pesticide build-up/intensive farming or monoculture/others House-building – Named example and impact, e.g. land clearance/habitat loss/others Industry – Named example and impact, e.g. oil/SO_2/thermal pollution/others **Named example = 1 mark** **Impact on biodiversity = 1 mark**	2	In choice questions such as this it is worth spending a minute writing down key terms or phrases that come to mind to determine which one will give you the most marks
11	a)		Time spent kicking/collecting Strength of kicking Time of day Net mesh size Distance between marked area and net **Any two, 1 mark each**	2	Not the usual variable that you are often asked about. However, the same principle applies – you are trying to consider factors that could affect the sample and so should be controlled and kept the same

Practice Paper B			Section 2 Paper 2		Commentary with hints and tips
Question			**Expected answer**	**Marks**	
	b)		Some invertebrates could pass through the net/mesh Some invertebrates could pass/ be carried outside the net Some invertebrates are not dislodged/remain attached to stones Some invertebrates are wrongly identified Not enough repeats were carried out **Any one**	1	Some questions set in an unfamiliar context require you to think carefully about the procedure and what is going on
	c)	**(i)**	10–99	1	Fairly straightforward selecting information question
		(ii)	Mayfly larvae	1	Sample 1 is located before the sewage enters and so is unpolluted. The mayfly larvae do not occur at any point after the sewage enters
	d)		Indicator species	1	Another key term for the flash cards
12	**a)**	**(i)**	Used to transfer useful genes from unrelated species into plants	1	Simply a case of locating the relevant information or statement to answer the question. No need to put it in your own words
		(ii)	Toxic proteins might be produced **OR** Antibiotic-resistance genes may be transferred to human gut bacteria	1	Notice that 'unforeseen effects' would not be enough and you are required to read further to pick out specific examples
	b)	**(i)**	Increased crop yield/crops not eaten or harmed by pests or equivalent **OR** Spend less money buying/ applying pesticide	1	This answer involves you applying your knowledge of the pest-resistant crops to consider the advantage to the farmer
		(ii)	Reduced/no impact of pesticide Reduced toxicity/avoids pesticide accumulation in food chains	1	This answer involves you applying your knowledge of the pest-resistant crops to consider the advantage to the environment
	c)		Control of pests using natural predators/parasites/others	1	The term 'biological' tells us that living organisms are involved in this type of control
[END OF PRACTICE PAPER B ANSWERS]					

Practice Paper C

Section 1

Practice Paper C	Section 1 Objective Test		Commentary with hints and tips
Question	Answer	Marks	
1	C	1	Osmosis is water movement in which the water molecules move down a concentration gradient and so it does not require energy – it is passive
2	B	1	When plant cells lose water their contents shrink. The shrunken contents pull away from the cell wall as shown in the diagram. Being in a strong salt solution will cause water loss by osmosis
3	B	1	mRNA carries a complementary copy of DNA codes from the nucleus to the ribosome
4	D	1	In degradation reactions a substrate is **broken down** into products
5	A	1	In genetic engineering, a required gene is removed from a source chromosome and inserted into a bacterial plasmid
6	A	1	The number of bubbles of oxygen is related to the rate of photosynthesis. Lower light intensity from a more distant lamp would reduce the bubbling rate
7	D	1	You are not expected to know about potato reproduction. Each possible answer has to be checked individually and a ruler and highlighter will help
8	C	1	Since the respiration is aerobic, X has to be oxygen and the ATP-producing reaction is shown coupled to the main reaction
9	D	1	Only gametes can be haploid so it follows that meristems are diploid. Meristems are the sites of production of non-specialised cells that have yet to be differentiated
10	D	1	Heterozygous flies are Gg and produce both G and g gametes – a Punnett square used to work out the possible fertilisations shows one GG for every two Gg and one gg; any fly that contains a G allele will be grey, so the overall ratio would be three grey to every one black
11	A	1	Polygenic characteristics show a range of phenotypes rather than phenotypes that fall into clear-cut groups
12	B	1	Structure Y is a lacteal, which absorbs the products of fat digestion in the small intestine

Practice Paper C	Section 1 Objective Test		Commentary with hints and tips
Question	**Answer**	**Marks**	
13	**C**	1	Rings of cartilage hold airways open just like the strengthening rings of a vacuum hose. Mucus is sticky and traps microorganisms while cilia sweep the dirty mucus to the mouth
14	**B**	1	Arteries carry blood out of the heart and vessel X is on the right side so it must be the pulmonary artery. Veins return blood to the heart and vessel Y is on the left so it must be the pulmonary vein: **A**rtery – **A**way and Ve**in** – **in**
15	**D**	1	Valves prevent backflow of blood and this valve is between the chambers of the left side of the heart. Remember the left side is shown on the right of the diagram.
16	**C**	1	A straight definition of a biome here
17	**D**	1	It must be 4500 because 45 000 are fixed by the woodland and of this 40 500 are lost as heat
18	**A**	1	Add up all the quadrat results = 60, then divide by the number of quadrats: **60/12 = 5**
19	**A**	1	Pesticides increase yield by preventing crop losses to pests. They accumulate in the bodies of organisms over time
20	**B**	1	Remember that indicator species give information about the environment by their absence as well as their presence

Practice Paper C

Section 2

Practice Paper C			Section 2 Paper 2		Commentary with hints and tips
Question			**Expected answer**	**Marks**	
1	a)		X – mitochondrion = 1 Y – ribosome = 1	2	You should be able to answer this question either by recognising the organelle shapes or by knowing their functions
	b)	(i)	Made from different substances **OR** not made from cellulose	1	Cell wall structure in fungal cells is different from plant cells because fungal cell walls are not made from cellulose
		(ii)	Fungal cells do not have chloroplasts/carry out photosynthesis but green plants do	1	Fungal cells are very similar to plant cells but they never contain chloroplasts – the clue in the question is the reference to green cells
	c)		Enzymes break down substrates **AND** produce products/release energy needed by the fungus	1	This is a 'suggest' question – so you need to think widely about the answer. Fungi are decomposers and feed by releasing enzymes into the material they decompose
2	a)	(i)	Vertical axis scaled correctly **AND** labelled with units from data table	1	Use the same scale above zero as below it and take the label and units from the table. Draw bars accurately with a ruler.
		(ii)	Bars plotted accurately	1	
	b)	(i)	Same potato variety **OR** same volumes of solutions	1	Not many variables left to be controlled, but always remember in these questions that there will be some
		(ii)	Repeat at each concentration (and average the results)	1	Reliability is strengthened by repeating and very often the repeats would be averaged, so remember **ROAR** – **R**epeat and **O**btain an **A**verage to increase **R**eliability. In this case it is crucial to mention the repeat at each concentration
	c)		50 g/l = 1 Concentration midway between +5 gain and −5 loss of mass = 1	2	If the solution was equal in concentration to that in the tissue then no change in mass would be expected because there would be no concentration gradient down which water could move

Practice Paper C			Section 2 Paper 2		Commentary with hints and tips
Question			Expected answer	Marks	
3	a)		Prevent contamination by other species of microbe	1	The term contamination is useful here – other microbes would be a problem because they might compete for resources in the fermenter, have a damaging effect on the desired microbe, or even produce toxic substances
	b)	(i)	To maintain the optimum temperature for enzyme action	1	It is important to relate the temperature to the activity of enzymes
		(ii)	1 Oxygen present in the air bubbled in = 1 2 (aerobic) respiration = 1	2	Oxygen is present in air and allows aerobic respiration by microbes
	c)		glucose/sugar/amino acids/ others	1	The culture medium must be appropriate – liquid media are good in fermenters but solid agar is better in dishes. Glucose needed for energy or amino acids to produce protein
4	a)		adenine pairs with thymine guanine pairs with cytosine	1	The bases can be identified by their initial letters (A, T, G, C) and base pairing rules need to be mentioned. **A**pples in **T**rees + **C**ars in **G**arages is a nice tip!
	b)		Sequence/order of bases in the DNA molecule	1	The sequence of bases in DNA determines the sequence of amino acids in proteins
	c)		Carries a complementary copy of DNA/copy of the order of the bases in the gene = 1 from the nucleus to the ribosome = 1	2	Remember, the 'message' on messenger RNA is a complementary copy of the DNA code and the ribosomes are the sites of protein synthesis
5			1 Light trapped by chlorophyll (in chloroplasts) 2 Light energy converted to chemical energy/ATP 3 Water split into hydrogen and oxygen 4 Hydrogen attached to hydrogen acceptor 5 (Excess) oxygen diffuses from the cell **Any four, 1 mark each**	4	For extended responses, you have to focus in on a group of related facts – take your time on these questions. A mini-plan is a good idea
6	a)		Tissue	1	Similar specialised cells working together make up tissues
	b)	(i)	Carry oxygen round the body	1	Remember, the haemoglobin they contain binds **oxy**gen to form **oxy**haemoglobin

Practice Paper C			Section 2 Paper 2		Commentary with hints and tips
Question			**Expected answer**	**Marks**	
		(ii)	Biconcave shape **OR** large surface area **OR** no nucleus/organelles **OR** contain haemoglobin = 1 Increases surface area **OR** more efficient absorption/release of oxygen **OR** more space for haemoglobin **OR** binds and releases oxygen = 1 **Must match**	2	Many different adaptations to choose from here – make sure they match to the explanation of their effect
7	a)	(i)	X – sensory neuron **OR** Y – relay neuron **OR** Z – motor neuron = 1	1	These questions refer to a package of knowledge about the reflex arc – you need to learn the whole package for full understanding. Try putting the stages of the reflex arc into a flow chart. Remember: **SS** = Sense organ → Sensory neuron **MM** = Motor neuron → Muscle (effector)
		(ii)	Sensory neuron – carries impulse from receptor to CNS Relay neuron – carries nerve impulse from sensory to motor neuron Motor neuron – carries impulse from CNS to muscle/gland **Must match**	1	
	b)	(i)	Synapse	1	Electrical impulses carry messages along neurons but chemicals are needed for them to cross the gaps
		(ii)	Chemicals released into synapse/gap (transfer messages)	1	
	c)		Allows rapid response **AND** so avoids damage by intense heat	1	Need to mention the speed of response and specific threat posed by the stimulus – here it is intense heat
8	a)		To prevent evaporation of water into the air	1	If water escaped to the atmosphere, the experiment would be invalid because it would mean that water that was lost from the apparatus was not all transpired
	b)		To allow comparison of shoots of different sizes/leaf areas	1	It is very difficult to obtain shoots that have identical sizes of leaves and this method deals with this problem
	c)		(It may be) used as a raw material in photosynthesis **OR** stored in vacuoles to produce turgidity	1	The apparatus really measures water uptake, not transpiration, because water taken up might be either stored or used in photosynthesis
	d)		500%	1	0.2 units increases to 1.2 units, which is a 1.0 unit increase; then **1.0/0.2 × 100 = 500%** – remember, percentages can be higher than 100%
9	a)	(i)	94 deaths per 1000 births	1	Quite a bit of work to read all six bars and a calculator more or less essential: **180 + 72 + 56 + 48 + 88 + 120 = 564**, then **564/6 = 94**
		(ii)	1.1 to 2.5 kg	1	Drawing a line across the graph at 80 deaths per 1000 births makes this one quite easy

Practice Paper C			Section 2 Paper 2		Commentary with hints and tips
Question			Expected answer	Marks	
		(iii)	Not enough energy/not strong enough to survive birth/suckle/ keep warm	1	'Suggest' means that any reasonable answers would be accepted
		(iv)	Heaviest lambs have highest death rates	1	The evidence is in the histogram trend.
	b)		Nucleus of male gamete/sperm cell fuses with nucleus of female gamete/ovum/egg cell	1	It is the fusion of the two haploid nuclei that creates the diploid zygote
10	a)		Sectors of 50%, 25% and two of 12.5% = 1 Correct labels = 1	2	Pick out the mid-point of the circle and use your ruler to draw the lines to make the sectors. Do not include a label for Springtails as there were none found
	b)		2 : 5	1	Select 10 : 25 from the table and then find the lowest common factor and divide both sides by this value – **10/5 : 25/5 = 2 : 5**
	c)		Increases the reliability of the results/sampling process	1	The more samples that can be taken, the higher the reliability of the results obtained
	d)		Species that can fly **OR** attach to surfaces/are sessile are not caught	1	Pitfall traps are limited to sampling invertebrates that move along the surface
	e)		Temperature **OR** moisture/ rainfall **OR** light **OR** pH of soil	1	Almost any abiotic factor would do here
11	a)		Increased human population requiring increased food yield	1	There is pressure on farmers to use fertiliser to meet increased food demand
	b)		Lack of light	1	The thick layer of algae blocks light and prevents photosynthesis
	c)		Increased bacterial numbers cause decrease in oxygen concentration	1	Aerobic means oxygen-requiring
	d)		Increased fertiliser decreases biodiversity **OR** converse	1	An alternative to fertiliser may be GM crops
12	a)		Bacteria **OR** fungi	1	Organism X is converting protein in crops into ammonia, so must be a decomposer
	b)		Nitrite	1	In the decomposition cycle ammonia is converted into nitrites then on to nitrates
	c)		Denitrification	1	Many species of bacteria are crucial in the nitrogen cycle and process 1 is common in water-logged soils, which are denitrified because of that; other species such as those at 2 live inside plant roots and convert nitrogen in the air into nitrate
	d)		Nitrogen-fixing bacteria in plants/root nodules convert nitrogen gas to nitrates (within plants)	1	

Practice Paper C			Section 2 Paper 2		Commentary with hints and tips
Question			**Expected answer**	**Marks**	
13	**a)**		Geographical	1	The remoteness of the islands strongly suggests a geographical barrier formed by the Pacific Ocean
	b)		Mutation: Provides a source of new alleles/variation = 1 Natural selection: Best suited/ fittest survive **OR** survival of the fittest = 1 Survivors pass beneficial alleles/ mutations/genes on to offspring = 1	3	Try **I'M** a **N**ew **S**pecies to remember this story: **I**solation **M**utation **N**atural **S**election

[END OF PRACTICE PAPER C ANSWERS]